# THE SHETLAND PONY

*To My Wife*

# The Shetland Pony

Maurice Cox

Adam and Charles Black · London

First edition 1965
Second edition 1976
by A & C Black Ltd.
35 Bedford Row WC1R 4JH

© 1976 A & C Black Ltd.

ISBN 0 7136 1547 8

Filmset and printed in Great Britain by
BAS Printers Limited, Wallop, Hampshire

# Contents

1 Early History     1
2 Nineteenth Century in Shetland     13
3 Shetland Now     24
4 Breeding     42
5 Studs     55
6 Management     71
7 Uses     89
8 Showing     107
9 Exports     120
   Conclusion     135
   Bibliography     136
   Index     137

Early Christian sculptured stone from Papil, Burra Isle

# Acknowledgements

Douglas Bentley, page 100; Mary Evans
Picture Library, page 59; Leslie Lane, page
135; Clive Hiles, page 90; Ministry of Defence,
page 104; National Coal Board, page 102;
National Museum Edinburgh, pages 17, 93,
94; Pony Magazine, pages 11, 75; Scottish
Tourist Board, page 2; Studio Maxwell,
page 25, 54; Zetland County Library &
Museum, pages v, 3, 12, 38, 63, 88, 123

# *Preface*

For over fifty years no book on the Shetland pony has been published in this country and much interesting and valuable information about the breed might be lost if not recorded now.

The well known studs of the early days of the Stud Book and their owners are merely names to most of the present day breeders and little is generally known about them, except from the records in the Stud-books of what they bred, sold and bought and the prizes they were awarded. My wife and I had the privilege of knowing some of these personalities, of seeing their studs and receiving from them valuable help and advice, therefore it is possible to record something more personal about them.

Extracts from works by various authors of early books on Shetland have already been freely quoted in articles and papers on the Shetland pony. I make no apology for referring briefly to these, but I have succeeded in finding some original and previously unquoted references to the breed, which I think are of interest. Some of the oft repeated sayings and references I have queried or contradicted in the light of present knowledge.

The opinions and views expressed in this book are my own, except where stated to be otherwise; that every owner or breeder will agree with them all is not to be expected, but possibly they may prove to be a basis from which to work.

I would like to record my sincere appreciation for the help and co-operation from the many who so kindly answered my queries and who provided valuable information.

To my wife I owe a very great debt of gratitude for her unfailing patience, help and encouragement and the straight-forward criticism she has given, without which it is extremely doubtful that this work would have been undertaken.

In this revised edition it has been possible to give some additional information about the past history of the breed and to record a few facts concerning the establishment of the Shetland pony in other countries.

MAURICE C. COX
*1976*

# *Foreword*

Between the Wars, Shetland ponies were literally valueless; many in Shetland were shot and such Island Breeders as continued stopped entering produce in the Stud Book and didn't bother to use registered stallions.

Maurice and Betty Cox have been breeding Shetland Ponies for fifty years, first in Dorset and later in Kirkcudbright.

They had always been interested in the condition of the Shetland Pony in its native place, and after the Second World War they started to study how the breeding of Shetland Ponies in the Islands could be re-established.

The great majority of the ponies left in Shetland belonged to crofters, and they were run on that 90% of Shetland land that is Common Grazings. As any shareholder in a Grazing could run any sort of stallion he liked on the grazing, this set a problem that had to be solved before any kind of progress was possible. As luck would have it, in 1955 Parliament established the Crofters Commission to assist the development of crofting in all its aspects and the Commission were persuaded to lay it down that only stallions registered in the Shetland Pony Stud Book could be run on Common Grazings in Shetland.

The next problem was to find registered stallions to run on the Common Grazings; as there were effectively none in Shetland they would all have to be shipped in from the South.

*The Shetland Pony*

The livestock section of the Department of Agriculture, who were also anxious to re-establish pony breeding in Shetland, produced a scheme for paying a premium for stallions offered for use on Common Grazings in Shetland, and offered to subscribe part of the premium. After a very considerable struggle, the Coxs persuaded the Stud Book Society to subscribe the balance of the premium, and the Stallion Premium Scheme was under way.

The next problem was to provide registered mares for the stallions, bearing in mind that there were no registered mares in Shetland. The Stud Book Society was persuaded to allow Shetland Pony Mares in Shetland to be accepted for registration in the Stud Book for a limited period if they were considered suitable after inspection. This was fine, but of course it meant that every owner of a mare in Shetland could require that it be physically inspected and, crofters being as they are, the inspectors had to go to the pony. This was certainly the most arduous part of the whole rescue operation for the Coxs. They were the only qualified people who were able and willing not only to go to Shetland, but to visit isolated crofts on islands off the Shetland Mainland, where roads were bad, night stops inevitable and accommodation not exactly luxurious. Over the next fifteen years, the work was done, but the effort and discomfort involved is well understood and gratefully appreciated throughout Shetland.

The programme that would re-establish quality pony breeding in Shetland had been planned and established. The Coxs' final gift was to persuade the Stud Book Society to run Pony Sales in Shetland, and to persuade buyers from America and Europe as well as the United Kingdom to brave the journey to Unst and Lerwick in October.

Despite one or two weather disasters, they succeeded in this, as in all else and everyone in Shetland says 'Thank You'.

R H W Bruce CBE
*1976*

selves, under, as a rule, unfavourable conditions. Obviously the environment may play a double part, it firstly may arrest growth by failing to provide sufficient food and shelter and secondly it may eliminate the individual which by growing beyond a certain size, require during times of stress more food and shelter than available.'

It is almost certain that there was a further infusion of the 13.2 h.h. 'cob' type in Shetland. Whilst excavating the Viking settlement at Jarlshof, Miss Platt found bones of ponies. These were less numerous than those found in the earlier settlement but in sufficient quantity to demonstrate that although the animals were not large they exceeded in size the small ponies of the present time.

There were many Viking raids during the fourth, fifth and sixth centuries A.D. and it is unlikely that ponies would have been taken on these forays. However, when emigrating on a larger scale the Scandinavians sought new lands not only in the Caspian and Black seas but in Central Europe, the British Isles, Iceland and Greenland. It appears that the Viking warriors rode stallions and undoubtedly those that settled in the northern isles would also have brought their mounts.

On the island of Bressay, near the ancient church of Culbinsburgh, a sculptured stone was found in the mid-nineteenth century depicting a priest or monk seated on a small pony. Wainwright considered that this stone 'probably commemorates a Scandinavian and it was certainly cut after the Scandinavians had arrived in the northern isles and after Christianity had appeared among them'. This would date the sculpture to about the end of the ninth century.

While grave digging beside the disused church of Papil on Burra Isle, three ornamental stones were unearthed: Wainwright considered these to be the finest sculptures of the Celtic and Norse period yet found in Shetland. One of these stones shows three priests or monks preceding and one following a peak hooded figure seated on a pony. This pony is similar in shape and size to that on the Bressay Stone, and has a high head carriage and light bone. Assuming the human figures to be those of a normal stature the height of the pony would be approximately forty inches. This stone probably dates from the end of the ninth century A.D. and shows sculpture of Pictish tradition which had survived Scandinavian influence.

The bones and sculptures provide sure evidence that small ponies have been domestically used in Shetland for more than 1000 years and probably much longer. The domestication of the breed may be presumed from the fact that bones of other animals found in the settlements of the sixth to first centuries B.C. had been split for the extraction of marrow, whereas those of the ponies had not.

At one time it was assumed that the drawings in the well-known 'Pony Frieze' in the caves at Lascaux in France depicted ponies similar to those of Shetland breed and that some were piebald. However, further research proved that the so-called ponies are in fact horse foals and the piebald markings of some are due to flaking patches of rock.

Summarising the evidence we find that the Shetland pony probably originates from two types – the 13.2 h.h. 'cob' type Tundra horse and the 12.2 h.h. 'Mountain' pony type from southern Europe. The latter in turn was later crossed with the pony brought by the Celts – a breed formed by the crossing of the above 'Mountain' pony with the 'Oriental' horse. Then, after another few centuries, there was a further infusion of the 13.2 h.h. 'cob' type of stallion with the Vikings.

There is virtually no written work about the Shetland pony until the sixteenth century and these are mostly judgements recorded in the Court Books concerning theft or unlawful borrowing of ponies.

In 1469 Princess Margaret of Norway was betrothed to the young King James of Scotland. Her father, Christian I of Denmark, agreed to pay as dowry 60,000 Rhenish florins of which 10,000 were to be in cash. But within a year Orkney was pledged for the remaining 50,000. However, only 2,000 florins were paid in cash so the Norwegian rights in Shetland were pledged for the balance of 8,000 florins.

The conditions of the pledge were that Shetland was to remain under the direct rule of the sovereign and that the laws and ancient privileges of Scandinavian rule should remain. Less than a hundred years later however, Robert Stewart, Bishop of Holyrood, an illegitimate son of James V, was granted a few of the Orkney and Shetland Isles and invested with the dignity of Sheriff of Shetland. In spite of the extremely oppressive unprincipled acts for which his nephew

James VI twice recalled him, he was created hereditary Earl of Orkney and Lord of Zetland.

The Court Books of Shetland first mention these ponies in writing. They record various offences and unlawful borrowing without the owner's permission which seems to have caused some trouble for we find that in 1603 at

> 'Soundbrughe Magnus Clarkis gude son has ridden ane horse of Robert Rattray over the two scattallis of Scatness and Lie'

and he had to pay a fine of 'Twyse XIS'.

It was illegal to cut hair off the tail of other persons' ponies. Although an act prohibiting this was passed in 1628, cases where fines were imposed for cutting tails are recorded as early as 1602 when,

> 'Vicentious Grevensoun, Hierome Christophersoun and Mongie Ronaldsoun hes rowit Captain Thomas Kynchtsonis horse tailes and thairfoir ilk ane of them are decernit to pay XI S Scottis and ordainis that nane row or cut ony manis horse tailis far this furthe, ilk person under paine of XLI.'

Captain Kynchtson was the Earl's Foud or Lawman so the choice of his horse was unfortunate.

A few cases of stealing ponies are mentioned such as in Unst in 1604 when David Sinclair was accused of the 'Stouth of ane horse stolen fra David Spens and ane meir alledgit stollen fra David Spenis bairns of fra the guid-wife of Vorisgert', or in Yell where Magnus Wischert was accused of taking 'ane horse fra Swynie Windois in Bud'.

The number of ponies and other stock some of the inhabitants of the islands possessed at the time of their death can be learnt from these records. Agnes Olasdochter, for example, a poor woman in Aithsting, had an estate worth only £20 3s. 4d. which included a half share of a mare, two cows and seven sheep. This is a far cry from the inventory of one Robert Sinclair, a member of a family called the Sinclairs of Brough in the district of Nesting during the sixteenth and seventeenth centuries. This family claimed nobility and its head assumed the title of Baron of Brough. Robert Sinclair at his death owned eighty-two horses and thirty-eight mares, as well as a great deal of other stock – 3,060 sheep and almost 200 head of cattle.

In 1633 a Captain John Smith visited the islands to make a report on Dutch exploitation of fishing off the islands. He makes a brief reference to the ponies stating that 'some were little bigger than asses'.

In 1700 one J. Brand visited these islands and the north of Scotland and wrote a fairly concise description of what he saw. Again it is the ponies' small size which seems to have struck him but he is also greatly impressed with their strength and how the owner can be carried by his pony 'and a woman behind him, eight miles forward and as many back'. He marvels how they live out in all weathers an 'never come into a House, but run upon the mountains in some places in flocks'; and as well as their hardiness he is impressed by their nimbleness. He also draws attention to their longevity, and it is interesting to note that 'those of a black colour are judged the most durable, and the pyeds not so good'. It is probably Brand who first expressed the belief that the ponies had to eat seaweed in winter to exist.

Thirty years later Thomas Gifford wrote a 'Historical Description of Zetland' in which he gives a brief account of the ponies, emphasizing again their small size and their extreme strength and mettle. He, too, stresses their hardiness and how little winter fodder they have, not because of the owner's wilful neglect, but because of the difficulties of securing sufficient food for oxen and cows for winter feeding.

In 1780 a naval surgeon visiting the islands records in his diary:

'Having met with the surgeon of the Helens Brigg, Mr Wardrope, we were furnished with little horses and set out over hill and moor, rock and stone. We trotted along brinks of dreadful precipices where I would not venture to trust myself on the best hunter in England. The motions of these little Shetland horses are so very quick and short that I made many narrow escapes from falling over their necks'.

Three days later he writes

'The horses in Zetland are of a remarkable small breed but exceedingly well shaped. They sell them at the rate of twenty or thirty shillings. They are well adapted to the country being surefooted and nimble. I have been amazed to see them trotting along briskly under the weight of a stout heavy man whom one would have thought just as capable of carrying them.'

His diary jottings suggest that this surgeon was considerably more knowledgeable about ponies or horses than earlier writers.

In about 1822 Samuel Hibbert M.D. F.R.S.E. paid three visits to Shetland and published the description of his travels in the islands. His real interests were the health of the inhabitants and geology and it would appear that he had little real interest in or knowledge of animals but like all the other writers he does mention their small size, strength and sagacity. Hibbert shows none of Brand's understanding of winter feed: he is appalled by their hard treatment in winter, how they are left outside and compelled to live on drift–ware left by the ebb.

The 1841 Statistical Account of Shetland contains some items concerning ponies which were contributed by the parish ministers in accounts of their parishes. The minister of Aithsting and Sandsting says that white, black, brown, grey, dun, cream chestnut and piebald ponies, varying in height from twenty-eight to forty-four inches, were kept in the parish but he states that they were little used and there is no attention paid to the breed. Curiously enough he says that gravel and spavin are the most common 'diseases': the latter seems strange, particularly as he says they did little work.

The ministers in Unst were disturbed that the size of pony was decreasing due to the 'best and stoutest being exported' and because stallions of the most puny size are allowed to go at large'. Other ministers say the same thing and stress that little or no attention is paid to breeding. Yet although they point out the deteriorating physique of the ponies they apparently make no suggestion as to how this situation might be altered. However, this question as reported by the ministers posed many problems for even if a crofter was willing and economically able to keep a good pony as a stallion, he was up against many difficulties. Firstly, he had to run his ponies on the scattald where other ponies belonging to other shareholders were also running. Now these other shareholders might not share his

9

views about breeding, or they might not bother, or they might not be friendly. So more than one shareholder had probably a better colt or stallion than his neighbour or perhaps he had been unable to sell one or two poor or indifferent colts so he had no alternative but to run them on the scattald. Therefore the good colts or stallions on the hill mingled with bad ones which were possibly more powerful and able to keep most of the mares. This meant that the better entires got few mares, and the owner who had good mares often had them served by some ugly scrub colt. This situation was aggravated by the dealers' lack of demand for bad or indifferent ponies.

In the 'General Observations' to these accounts, Laurence Edmonston M.D. of Buness, Unst, expresses similar views to those of the parish ministers. He also comes down heavily against crossbreeding:

> 'a pernicious practice has too much prevailed of crossing with larger and incongruous breeds from Scotland; and the progeny, as might be expected, displays all the bad points, with few of the good of the parents. A natural but rough antidote to these evils is, to some measure, to be found in bad seasons which fall with fatal severity on the degenerate.'

Dr Edmonston suggests that an improvement of the breed would be effected if all inferior males were removed and proprietors kept really good stallions in the various districts for the general use of owners of mares. Later on in the century this practice did come into use in a modified way but probably benefited the stallion owners' more in the first place than the breed in general. Later still, (as may be read of in another chapter), the Society, with the help of the Department of Agriculture for Scotland, started a more comprehensive scheme similar to that advocated by Dr Edmonston. He also points out the absence of roads and lays stress on the use of ponies with pack saddles for transporting goods when or where carriage by water is not possible.

It has been related how most early writers emphasise the lack of care in breeding, the prevailing poor winter conditions for animals in the northern isles and how both sheep and ponies had to rely on sea-ware to survive in winter. There is no doubt that in the past there may have been too many ponies in some areas for breeding was more

Foraging for food in the snow

or less uncontrolled. Nature alone regulated the population for severe winters, particularly after bad summers, brought starvation very near and emaciated stock were often unable to withstand the raging storms of winter. It was not due to wilful neglect but the physical and economical difficulties of providing sufficient fodder. Even today in Shetland and other hill and mountain areas the problem of winter feed looms large, particularly on smaller, poorer farms.

Few ponies had stables in winter. The little available timber in the islands, much of which was brought in by the sea, was used for rooves on human dwellings. It might be of interest here to mention that in Shetland generally the croft and small houses were low and the rooves normally were low pitched for this not only economised on timber but also resisted the wind. The lairds' houses were high but covered a small base area: this also economised on timber.

As already mentioned lack of stabling is no inconvenience to the ponies for shelter can easily be found. Moreover, the difficulty of finding bedding is eliminated. Any straw on a croft is far too valuable as fodder to be used for anything else.

Shetlanders often talk of their horses instead of ponies. The use of the word 'Sheltie' is seldom heard on the islands and seems more common in Scotland where it is often applied to any small pony. Brand, writing in 1701, mentions the use of this name and Campbell, writing half a century later, does the same. It seems it is derived from the Icelandic word 'Hyjalti' for a Shetlander.

Tingwall women on a shopping expedition to Lerwick – late nineteenth century

# 2
# *Nineteenth Century in Shetland*

During the nineteenth century considerably more was written about the Shetland pony.

More ponies were being sent off the islands as vessels large enough to carry a few ponies were calling at Lerwick or Scalloway and the demand in Europe and Britain was higher.

Dr Edmonston mentions that in 1809 no less than 150 ponies were exported; records show that in 1824 ninety-two were shipped and in 1825 a further 140. Doubtless more were sent out that were not noted. Fishing vessels from Holland and other European ports are known to have taken some and probably a number were shipped to Hamburg which was Shetland's principal trading port in Europe.

These ponies were exported for various purposes: for children, for circuses, for exhibitions and for ornamental use in gentlemen's parks. For example the estate records of 1815 at Ickworth, Suffolk, the seat of the Marquis of Bristol, mention that there are Shetland ponies in the park.

There is an article called 'A Stranger's Opinion of Shetland' in the *Shetland Advertiser* of May 1862 which speaks of their use in Shetland for agricultural purposes. It is doubtful, however, whether the writer of the article really knows the Shetland pony or whether the animals written about are what are called 'work ponies' – that is larger animals of various origins but often of Shetland pony cross. The writer mentions that one sees larger horses of the Orkney or Scotch breed and he also states that smaller land-holders till their land by manual labour. One cannot help thinking that he had little knowledge of ponies for he states 'The Shetland horses foal in the month of April or May and generally bring forth one at a time'. (!) He also tells us that 'The foals stand the climate well and are fed on grass'.

He reports that the value of a pony ranged from £5 to £8 except for the best which fetched £10 to £12. This was a considerable increase in value from about twenty years previously when the price of a pony ranged from £1 10s. to £6.

Considering the value of money in those days these prices of £5 to £12 were quite good: after all, a herd boy's wage in the islands at that time was from fifteen to twenty shillings per year with bed and board. Mr Ian E. M. Sandison states that during his great grandfather's and grandfather's time the average price of a pony could pay the annual wage of a stockman and during the time of his father it would cover one quarter.

Although some ponies were used for agricultural work it seems that the ox was fairly frequently used: most large farms had either oxen, small horses or both for use in ploughing and other slow work. One must remember that there were virtually no roads in Shetland until well after the mid-nineteenth century. As the wheel was not generally in use, most produce and all the peat was transported on the backs of ponies if transport by boat was not possible.

In 1829 a Faroese official, Christian Ployen, visited Shetland during his stay in Scotland and wrote of his experiences in a book published in Copenhagen in 1840. On arrival at Lerwick he and his host got into a small four-wheeled gig drawn by a Shetland pony and 'to my great astonishment the little animal trotted off with us . . .' Later he writes

'I had despised the Shetland pony before I mounted him, but I soon got great respect for him. Little he was, no doubt, even less than most of ours, (Faroese) but he was used to carry a rider, and was shod on his fore feet, a very necessary provision for carrying a burden over the stoney roads of Shetland or of Faroe'.

In describing one of his tours in Shetland he writes '. . . and though the road in many places was extremely bad, and the ponies were small, we proceeded at a tolerably brisk pace'.

Previous to the date of the quoted article in the *Shetland Advertiser* an Act of Parliament had been passed which prohibited children working in coal mines. These children had been employed in pulling coal tubs along the tunnels many of which were too low for even a child to stand upright. Almost immediately there was a demand for the Shetland pony to go down the mines and haul tubs, for they seemed strong and small enough for the task.

This demand from the pits caused their increased value. The 'Druid' (H. H. Dixon) states that over 500 ponies were taken for the pits every year and the prices he states are much in line with those mentioned previously. However, he goes into considerably more detail. A two-year-old colt fetched £5 10s., a more mature pony fetched £8 to £10.

Only male ponies were bought for underground work for the mixing of sexes below ground and at work would have been unsatisfactory. Moreover the mares were required to remain on the scattalds to breed and they were the ponies that did the work in the islands, for they were used for transport and flitting the peats, often with foal at foot. The 'Druid' also gives estimates of the numbers shipped: he reckons the annual total was about 500 yet in some years the grand total must have been considerably more. In addition to those colts and entires going direct to the pits a certain number with some mares were sent to the north-east of England where the Coalmasters started breeding these ponies on farms adjacent to the mines. As is mentioned in a later chapter many ponies were shipped direct to the U.S.A. where there was also a demand but it is not certain whether these are included in the 'Druid's' totals.

In 1864, in a letter from Holyrood Palace, P. Laurenson of Gremister Farm, Lerwick, was advised that the sum of £19 7s 6d had been paid into the bank for ponies which had arrived in good health: £4 10s for a small pony, £14 10s for a chestnut and white pair and 7s 6d for three bridles. The ponies for Holyrood Palace were for Queen Victoria's establishment in Scotland.

We learn from the 'Druid' in *Field and Fern* that Her Majesty had a pair of cream duns for her phaeton at Windsor sent down from the stud of Mr Balfour of Shapinsay in the Orkney Isles. This stud had been founded at the end of the eighteenth century and is actually the only stud of Shetland ponies mentioned as such by any writer up to that date. We are told that the mares were dun, brown and a mealy grey, and a chestnut stallion is described thus: 'North Unst has furnished them with one of the choicest jewels'. The 'Druid' also tells us that in May and October ponies were rounded up for dealers to choose from. He remarks that the best ponies come from Unst, but like earlier writers, he attacks breeders for their careless attitude to breeding and their concentration on foal getting at the expense of quality of sire.

It seems true that indifferent sires were commonly used but the dealers were often to blame for they were frequently anxious to take away the best animals. In the mid-nineteenth century Shetland had just emerged from a hard, disastrous spell and there was widespread poverty throughout the islands. A foal was an essential part of a crofter's economy.

Although a considerable number of ponies were exported, there must have been a large surplus of male ponies running on the hills, before the advent of the really heavy demand from the coal mines. Therefore any mare or filly might easily get in foal to some scrub entire. There seems to be no record or mention anywhere of the fate of the male superfluity, so it must be assumed that those which were not in good health probably succumbed during a hard stormy winter through illness or injury. Dr Edmonston referred to the fatal effect on the degenerate in bad seasons.

With the boom in demand for colts and stallions the dealers were as anxious as the coal owners to procure the best types and consequently most of the best probably left the islands except those which were aged, being considered unsuitable for breaking to harness and underground work. However there were two or three dealers who instead of sending the very best to the north of England kept a few stallions to run on scattalds with provisos that they should be offered first refusal of the foals. This, though much to the dealers' advantage, did ensure that a reasonably good entire was available to some of the mares. Sometimes a merchant or a dealer might supply a crofter with a mare but the dealer would have first offer of the foal: this system was known as 'halvers'. Some proprietors also took more interest in the stallions and tried to help to improve the stock.

Donald McAdie, who looked after the Londonderry ponies, with a sick foal – 1898

In addition to the studs being formed by Coalmasters in north-east England, Lord Londonderry, in the early 1870s, started one in Shetland. This had begun at Seaham Harbour in County Durham, where Shetland ponies had been used as pit ponies since 1850. Ponies were carefully selected from the islands and bred expressly to fill the demand for pit ponies in the Londonderry collieries. The ideal pony was a strong low animal with 'as much weight as possible and as near the ground as it can be got'. Although a number of strains did become long, low, draught animals, many ponies did not ever reach this objective, so the managers purchased those ponies which were nearest their mark. The Shetland pony had never been a draught pony and was different in characteristics and conformation from the desired animal for the pits. However, it possessed courage, strength and willingness. The managers bought those ponies which were nearest their ideal and through careful and selective breeding evolved a suitable animal for their purposes. It must be remembered, however, that the pony was still essential to the crofter, not only as a source of cash or income but also to transport produce and ensure that peat for winter firing was safely stacked beside the croft.

As well as the absorption by the pit trade of many male ponies two years old and over there was also a growing interest in the breed in other parts of Great Britain and abroad, particularly in North America. Some ponies were used for children to ride and drive and were an attraction running in parks; others earned their keep by working in large gardens and on farms; others still drew bath-chairs by the sea and at inland spas.

It is difficult to estimate the total number of Shetland ponies in the islands at any given time. We do know that in 1870 the total number of all horses and ponies was 4851 but there are no means of telling how many were really Shetland ponies nor how the figure was attained. Twenty years later the number had decreased by over 800, presumably because of demand. Considering that the estimated number of ponies in the islands in 1822 was 10,000, the decrease is phenomenal. It was probably at about this time that the sheep population increased as that of the ponies diminished.

It is to the credit of certain interested and astute men that in 1890 a Shetland Pony Stud Book Society was formed, the first native pony breed society. The Marquis of Londonderry was President and the Honorary Secretary was George Bruce of Aberdeen. Five of those who promoted this lived in Shetland – John Bruce of Sumburgh; Gilbert Anderson, Hillswick; Anderson Manson, Laxfirth; Alexander Sandison, Uyeasound and J. J. R. Meiklejohn, Bressay, while Gavin Haddan of Dalmuinzie, R. McDonald, the Factor of Cluny Estate, James Duncan, Inverness and Robert Brydon, Seaham Harbour, were the remaining members of the Committee.

The first volume of the Stud Book was published in 1891. It contains entries of 408 mares having had produce before 1 September 1890 and forty-eight stallions foaled before 1 January 1886. This volume also contains three very interesting articles by J. M. Goudie, J. J. R. Meiklejohn and R. Brydon. The names of 111 members are listed of whom the majority are crofters, although most of the ponies entered are not owned by them. The volumes of the following few years also contain a number of foundation stock as well as produce from the ponies already entered.

The largest proportion of ponies are under 40″ in height. Six stallions are entered at 42″ and a few mares and two stallions are recorded as going under the stick at 34″.

Apart from a year or two during war or depression the Stud Book has been published annually, varying in size according to the number of breeders and the state of the market. The office of Secretary to the Society changed occupancy three times until from 1908–9 Robert Walker held office for many years. After his retirement his firm, Walker and Duncan, continued as Secretaries to 1953–4; then Tom H. F. Myles took over and the office was moved from Aberdeen to Perth. In 1966 Tom Myles resigned and Duncan M. Patterson was appointed in his place, with his office in Montrose.

It might be appropriate here to mention the vastly increased membership of the Society during recent years – particularly since 1970 – and in this, the eighty-fifth year of the Society, the number of members must surely be higher than ever before. One result has been the increase in size of the Stud Books.

During the last ten years or so one or two small bodies or organisations have been formed with the aim of furthering the breed. The Shetland Pony Breeders Club was formed by Miss N. du Port in the 1960s and she also published for a short time a useful little magazine in conjunction with the Society and the Club.

On the island of Unst breeders and owners formed a Society to discuss matters concerning ponies there and a few years later a similar association was started on Mainland in an effort to co-ordinate pony affairs with the parent Society. These local groups can be of assistance to the Secretary and the Society's Council, but naturally the main business and direction must be approved and prescribed by that ruling body.

Up to 1905 it had been possible to enter mares in the Stud Book without a previous generation being registered, but even so when the Council of the Society decided to close the Stud Book, many breeders in the islands had still failed to register their ponies. In the autumn of 1908 the Society received a request from the Zetland County Council asking them to reopen the Stud Book as there was a strong feeling in Shetland that this was essential since breeders in the county had pure bred ponies which they were now unable to enter in the Book. The Council agreed to reopen the Stud Book, as it was estimated that there might be 1000 mares in Shetland alone eligible on inspection for registration. Regulations for inspection were drawn up and a mere five members of Council appointed to carry out the task. In fact the estimate of 1000 mares was over optimistic. 384 mares were passed for entry in Volume XXI and the Society benefited by the addition of 110 new members, over half of whom were Shetland residents. Actually the thousandth mare to be approved by inspection was entered in Volume XLIX, almost thirty years after the first inspections. 2145 inspected mares were entered in the book before the Council decided once again that it should be closed after 1971, the latter 1000 being recorded in slightly over half the time of the first 1000.

It seems likely that this request in 1908 by the County Council for the opening of the Stud Book was instigated by interested persons who were engaged in the export of ponies to the U.S.A. and Canada. These countries would not allow the import of ponies that were not registered unless a heavy import duty was paid. Registered animals in sufficient quantity just could not be found. At about the same time a few residents in Lerwick and three or four living elsewhere in the Islands decided to form a rival Stud Book Society which was only open to resident breeders in Shetland. Only four of the twenty members of the Committee of Management owned ponies. The whole object of this 'Shetland Islands Pony Stud Book Society' was to issue export certificates for ponies being shipped to the U.S.A. and Canada. One of its principal organisers had been in serious trouble with the original Society; legal action was taken and in consequence he was debarred from making entries in the Stud Book and obtaining export certificates. There was no love lost between the two Societies. However, this feeling was exacerbated when the United States Government refused to recognise this new Society: consequently the export certificate issued by it was invalid there and duty had to be paid on imported ponies. The Canadian Government, on the other hand, did recognise the new Society which enabled ponies to be imported duty free.

These volumes (1910–13), four in all, are lists of ponies with rather meaningless notes on stallions and mares, a list of ponies which had changed hands at home as well as for export, lists of members and so on. There are only one or two photographs and although quite well produced they are of little value as Stud Books. It might be that this new Society received more support from crofter breeders than it would have done if the original Society had been more sympathetic to these members. For it now appears that they had little support apart from that of the two prominent and helpful Council members resident in Shetland – Messrs Gilbert Anderson and Anderson Manson and possibly R.W.R. MacKenzie who visited the islands.

The outbreak of war in 1914 virtually ended the export trade and changed the situation. For without this trade the Shetland Islands Pony Society was redundant and it faded out.

In 1897 a 'Congested Districts, Scotland Act 1897', was a measure brought in to help districts too crowded to support their population. This Board issued grants and also gave powers to the Board of Agriculture for Scotland to purchase large farms and estates in the Highlands and islands to divide into holdings. Under this act the B.O.A.S. was able to form a stallion scheme: owners of nine stallions were given premiums or grants to make these stallions available for mares owned by crofters. Although we have little information about this scheme we know there was a keen demand for ponies at this time and a shortage of stallions, certainly of good ones, for serving mares. It seems that until 1915 these serving stallions did not have to be registered in the Stud Book nor was there any standard of excellence. Some were kept on tethers and mares brought to them for service which meant more or less constant attendance by the owner or other person to supervise the service and collect the fee but in one or two districts the stallions were travelled. In 1915 580 mares were stated to have been served and in 1925 690 mares were served. The scheme was discontinued in 1932 owing to heavy cuts in expenditure by the Treasury. Fees for service and numbers of mares previous to 1915 cannot be traced.

There is unfortunately a considerable lack of written information about ponies in Shetland at almost any period and much is conjecture. Possibly the most controversial question is whether there was more than one type of pony on the islands. It appears from authoritative statements that there was, at any rate after the turn of the century, but by then the breeding of ponies for the pit trade had been in progress for thirty years. It is possible, in fact highly likely, that it was this process which had formed the two types which R.W.R. Mac-Kenzie described – 'one a thick dray-horse type, the other more blood-like, which may be called the saddle type.' Dr and Mrs Douglas classify the types as 'purely Scandinavian' and 'an Oriental type'. Mr Ian Sandison reckons there were three types of pony, the third being very small but this is open to argument for these small ones could well be merely a branch of one of the other two. Mr John (Sheepy) Smith maintained that there were two types – the lighter higher type for riding, flitting peat and similar work and the heavy boned, straight-shouldered sort which was wanted for the pits. In 1915, in *Livestock of the Farm*, Professor C. Bryner Jones wrote

> 'There are two types amongst Shetlands, one with a coarse head and collar filling, rather than saddle shoulders; and the other with smart blood-like head and riding shoulders. As there have been no importations of stallions it is probable that this variation is due to the difference of individual traits common in all breeds and there it may be left.'

All these references to two types were made by authorities with knowledge of the Shetland pony, but all after various people had been breeding many for the pit trade. None of the authorities writing previous to 1850 mention two or more types. Surely Edmonston would have mentioned this even if the various ministers in their reports did not? Moreover, the well known 'Druid' (H. H. Dixon) who visited Shetland to gain information and wrote on horses, ponies, cattle and sheep throughout the British Isles would have drawn attention to any great variation of type let alone two or more.

The cause for slight differences between ponies from some scattalds and others was the 'lack of care in breeding' to which more than one minister drew attention. Probably Lord Londonderry's managers were able to pick out some heavier, coarser types and breed closely to these, so that within two or three generations a heavier, straight-shouldered sort was evolved and which stayed reasonably close to type; although, as R.W.R. MacKenzie affirmed, one did get an occasional reversion from one type to another.

The possibility of crossing with another breed has been raised but this seems unlikely. The scattalds in many parts of the islands are, as regards ponies at any rate, fairly well self-contained; when one brings the different islands into the question such a possibility of outcross throughout the islands is remote. For example, how could a Norwegian stallion, running possibly in Walls, affect the ponies in Burrafirth or Westing in Unst? Furthermore we have learnt from Edmonston and other more recent authorities that 'foreign' blood, in the way of crosses, does not survive sufficiently to influence the true native animal.

We have a strong evidence of this in the island of Fetlar where the laird at one time introduced an Arab stallion and the Department of Agriculture decided at a later date that a Highland pony stallion would be an advantage! Today there is no trace of either of these in the Shetland ponies there either in type or in size. Certainly fifteen years ago there were a number of plain Highland cross mares but now the stock appears to be pure Shetland.

To return to the peak period of breeding pit ponies. The photographs of groups of ponies at Lord Londonderry's stud on Bressay give little or no evidence of a cloddy, heavy type of pony: generally they are a good boned, reasonably heavy sort and some of the mares are certainly the light type used for peat flitting and the like.

# 3

# *Shetland Now*

It would be difficult to say exactly how many ponies are in the Shetland Isles at present. One can only arrive at a probable total by examining various available figures, none of which are likely to be completely accurate. However it can be assumed that the total is much larger than it was in the early 1960s. If various factors are taken into consideration it is probable that the total number of Shetland ponies in the islands is around 1000.

The Department of Agriculture for Scotland require that every June and December each occupier of an agricultural holding should complete a return of livestock on his holding. As so few horses are now used for agricultural purposes the number of horses or ponies on holdings is only asked for every five years. They are asked to state the number of horses used for agricultural or horticultural work, (any figures for this are not at all likely to include Shetland ponies) and to give the total number of all other horses and ponies. In 1965 the total return was 674 which appears to be the lowest ever recorded and even in 1970, the last available return shows only an increase of forty-five to 719. Naturally other horses and ponies than Shetlands have been included in these figures both recently and in the past, so it would appear that these others have died. As some owners of ponies do not occupy an agricultural holding their ponies would not be counted. In addition there might be errors in the returns through misunderstanding or carelessness, not wilful intent.

Mare with twin colt foals

In the 1974 sales at Lerwick and Baltasound 555 foals are cata-
logued. This is approximately the same number entered for these
sales for the previous few years: therefore allowing for some foals
not entered for sale, others sold privately and a few fillies kept on to be
bred from, it would appear that every mare in the islands had a foal
each year!

If the total number of foals entered for the Baltasound and Lerwick
sales twelve or fifteen years ago is compared with those of recent
sales, a terrific upsurge of numbers is apparent. In 1959 the numbers
for both sales amounted to about 210 ponies, and even in 1965 all
ponies entered from Unst, Fetlar and Mainland totalled just under
350.

1000 ponies is of course much lower than the figures given years ago, in fact lower than the Department's return for the years immediately following the War. It must be remembered, however, that the higher numbers given earlier were when ponies were being used for work and there was a steady market, though not at high prices, for all the colt foals for the coal mines. Dealers would buy these foals and take them south to run in large numbers on rough grazings or hills until they were old enough to be sold for underground work.

Now the pony is little used on its native islands: it is kept for interest and pleasure and the income that may be brought in by the sale of foals. It must be remembered by those who do not know the Shetlanders that most of the pony owners and breeders, certainly in Unst and Fetlar, are descendants of those who have had ponies for generations. In many cases the pony is something that they feel that they must keep; it may not cost much to do so but some small return for that and the time and trouble is naturally welcome. If, however, the numbers continue to increase or even remain static there is a danger of a saturated market. After all, the more ponies that are bred the more potential breeding ponies are on the market, and sometime the new breeders to whom so many ponies have been sold will also be producing ponies for sale.

Numerous people now owning Shetland ponies do not know of the desperate situation of breeders on the islands during the years of depression between the Wars, when ponies were worthless. Many were taken to the banks and shot because the cost of shipping them to Aberdeen was often higher than the price realised and the owner received a bill instead of a cheque. It will be tragic if this happens again or if owners throughout the United Kingdom find that there is little or no market for their ponies. It is useless just to sit back and hope that these drastic circumstances will not arise, however, and every owner must give serious thought and take determined action to try and avert such disaster.

When the Premium Stallion Scheme was first started it was stressed by the Society that its aim was to improve the ponies' quality not quantity and this has been reiterated time and again by those responsible for administering the scheme. However in Shetland, as in the rest of the country, more breeders have sprung up and also some of the original breeders in Shetland have increased their stock: this has created a demand for ponies which would not have been there had the number of breeders remained static. In other words it is obvious that the Breed Society must welcome new members and breeders although explosions could become embarrassing.

There is a general improvement shown by ponies in the islands which must be attributed to the scheme and its example. There is room for further improvement, but that can be said wherever animals are bred.

At the present time everything appears to be unsettled and inflation is affecting most countries. It is therefore extremely difficult to try to forecast future developments for the Shetland pony and its breeders in Shetland or any other part of the world.

To return to the number of ponies on the islands: there was a slight increase after the last war, which was probably partly due to difficulty in shipping and sales during hostilities and also because some ponies were still used for work. In the early fifties, however, American and Canadian buyers became active and many ponies left the islands for export across the Atlantic. This resulted in a considerable reduction of the total.

It was at about this time that the livestock inspectors of the Department of Agriculture expressed concern for the low standard of the ponies in the islands. A deterioration was apparent, partly due to overseas demand which had absorbed most better animals and partly due to the lack of suitable good stallions; furthermore the pits had been asking for a pony around 42″ and one or two very indifferent entires of a leggy type had been used on mares in some districts. The Department, therefore, arranged for a few better class stallions from the north of Scotland to stand for service of crofters' mares. The stallions were kept by either a farmer or crofter and any mare owner could bring along a mare for service. In one or two cases the stallion was run in an enclosure or even a fenced scattald: this latter method meant that only shareholders' mares had access to the horse whilst the former method, when the stallion was often tethered or kept in a small enclosure, meant that mares had to be brought to him. This was not very satisfactory since not all mares in Shetland are quiet or wear halters: it probably therefore took time and trouble for the mares' owners to catch them, take them to the entire and then possibly find they were not ready for service when they got there. In fact this method meant that only quiet mares or those that were kept in-by were likely to be bred to these Department stallions. Nevertheless it was a real effort to improve the quality of the ponies.

The Department naturally expected that the Shetland Pony Stud Book Society might be interested in this effort. At first, however, the Council by a majority refused to be interested. They made the one concession that suitable mares, of sufficient merit and not exceeding 42″, in foal to one of those stallions placed by the Department, would be accepted by the Society as Inspected Stock: the livestock inspectors were authorised to do these inspections and for their own convenience place a numbered metal clip in the ear of an approved mare. Incidentally, these clips did lead to minor occasional trouble for grease and dead hair sometimes collected between the metal and the skin causing a local septic condition due to pressure and sometimes clips were pulled out by catching in long heather or on wire fences and tore the ear. A few years ago one saw an old mare or two with unsightly torn ears, but at the time of insertion it was a positive method of identification.

Meanwhile there were some Council members who were bitterly disappointed by the attitude shown by the President and others on the Council who maintained that those ponies left in the islands were of no use to the breed and that it was pointless trying to encourage the breeding of better ponies in the islands, although be it noted that only one or two of these men had ever been to the Shetland Isles. Apart from making the light concession of allowing Jimmy Dean to approve suitable mares for inclusion as Inspected Stock, they would have nothing to do with the Department's projected scheme for the improvement of Island ponies. However, Mr Dean, the chief livestock inspector in the north, was not discouraged and so it came about that a scheme was worked out which was presently put to the Council. Thanks to much preparatory activity and a change of mind by some Council members a Premium Stallion Scheme to be run in conjunction with the Department was evolved and accepted. Started in 1956, this Scheme has, with only minor additions or alterations, been in operation ever since.

It was essential, if the scheme was to run smoothly, that there must be liaison between the Society and the Stallion Custodians. My wife and I both went north to Shetland once or twice during the year and Tom Myles, the Society's Secretary, also made the journey more than once. In addition to the Stallion Scheme there were many mares to inspect. Weather conditions could be atrocious but at other times were delightful. We were always treated with genial sociability, even when a mare had to be refused acceptance due to its height or another fault. When the scheme was in its first infancy we called on crofters who we learnt had mares and scattald rights to try and estimate the amount of mares on a scattald and to see what sort of ponies they were: obviously it would make a difference to the stallion to be placed on the scattald. One or two of the crofters appeared slightly suspicious as to the reason for these calls. We were asked, 'Are you from the Department?' or 'Have you anything to do with the Department?' Whenever they were assured that we had nothing to do with that government body but were acting for the Shetland Pony Stud Book Society suspicion vanished and we received the information we sought.

Initially twelve stallions were placed on various scattalds or common grazings. Of these two only were on Mainland, three on Fetlar and the remainder on Unst. The following year one more stallion was added and by some re-arrangement Mainland was provided with four stallions for four grazings. In the next year still another stallion was added and in 1959 the number put out on the scattalds was eighteen. Since this date the number has been pretty constant at seventeen or eighteen stalions.

On Mainland five scattalds have the benefit of a Premium stallion. At one time six had this advantage, but the West Nesting hill area was removed from the scheme. In the north the big Eshaness grazing holds a number of good original type mares. They have, perhaps, more colour than is seen on some hills and foals from this district have usually sold well at the annual sales. In Walls, in west Mainland, there are two stallions with a further one on the adjoining Gruting scattald. On such a large area the mares are bound to vary considerably from the larger, leggy type to the small, possibly lighter boned, kind. Finally, there is the East Nesting grazing which is smaller, completely enclosed and away from any other hill on which there are ponies. Here, also, the type varies and probably about half are coloured ponies.

At the time of the scheme's formation the island of Yell had only a small handful of ponies eligible for the Stud Book: these were insufficient in number for the provision of a stallion.

Fetlar has been rather different from the other islands. More pony owners on Fetlar have taken advantage of the scheme than on other scattalds. The larger crossbred pony mares seem to have completely disappeared and two privately owned stallions are kept in addition to that of the proprietrix which is only used for her own unregistered mares. Three stallions were allotted to the island until a year or two ago, since when two were put out on the grazings. Theoretically this should be enough but it must be remembered that these mares on the hill follow a pattern of life very similar to the wild. One part of them will 'heft' or tie themselves to one area and another part to a different area of the hill. No stallion will be able to hold together both herds: consequently he will either stay with one herd or spend much time and energy travelling between the two and possibly doing his futile uttermost to join the two herds. So it comes about that a number of mares are missed and the foal return is lower than it should be.

Stallions on the scattalds should round up their mares and keep them reasonably close together. Most of them do so until late in the season when the mares are settled.

For two years a sale was held on Fetlar, but owing to the difficult, uncertain journey to the island and the reluctance of buyers to make the trip for the sale of thirty or forty ponies, it was arranged that they should be brought into Lerwick for the sale there.

Further north in Unst there are eight stallions sent out to scattalds each year. The South Unst grazings comprise the Muness, Uyeasound, Colvadale and Westing scattalds: on each of these one stallion is placed and as they are not divided from each other by fencing it is possible for ponies to wander from one scattald to another. Normally the mares stay very much to their own part of the hill. The greatest danger is that when a stallion has settled all his mares he may be tempted to wander off to find others and perhaps meet up with

Scattalds on which Premium Stallions are placed

another entire from the adjoining grazing. Then there can be serious trouble. Yet considering the possibility there are few instances of it actually taking place. In Unst, as on nearly all the Shetland scattalds, there is an assortment of mares, from the light boned leggy sort to some small, adequately boned ponies of good quality.

The Heoghs, just north of Baltasound, is an enclosed grazing which, from the road, looks rather forbidding with immense rocks and rocky outcrops. Nevertheless ponies do well on this hill and a suitable stallion will leave some useful foals from the fair-sized mares.

Clibberswick scattald, lying to the north-east of Haroldswick, is a hard hill bound on the easterly side by steep and dangerous cliffs to the sea. Two stallions were placed here. Here, too, is an assortment of mares which succeed in the difficult task of rearing foals in such hard conditions.

Ordale lies across the voe at Baltasound and is another hard grazing on which there are not many mares.

Finally, in the northern part of the island, lies the grazing of Ungersta. This is almost exclusively grazed by ponies although quite a large portion of it is heather. There have been two stallions placed here for a few years as some of the shareholders feel that there are too many mares running for one stallion to cope with.

This then is a brief description of the scattalds which are allotted a Premium stallion, although by no means all the ponies of Shetland are confined to these grazings. However, few ponies were not running on common grazings when this scheme started and it is of interest to note that on the southern portion of Mainland, south of the Nesting and Gruting scattalds, the only Shetland ponies being bred were those of Mr R.H.W. Bruce of Sand Lodge and Mr John Smith at Berry near Scalloway. These two breeders alone had stallions of their own for their own use. Odd colts had been running in the hills on other islands also, but most mare owners were only too pleased to see such superior stallions available for use on their mares.

The Crofters Commission, which had been most helpful when the scheme was inaugurated, arranged that grazing rules be altered where there was a Premium stallion to be put out, so that no shareholder was allowed to graze on the scattald any entire colt of a year or more. This insured that the Premium horse was able to round up and serve the mares as they came on without hindrance. In Fetlar, Sir Stanley Nicholson had his own stallion confined with his mares to his own hill; in Unst the position was similar with just one or two places where a stallion was run with the owner's mares. It must be remembered that throughout the islands a large number of mares were unregistered. A few had been inspected by the Department Inspectors and the odd one or two were second generation mares. However, once the scheme began and was favourably accepted by the crofter breeders, application for the inspection of mares came in freely and a great deal more interest was aroused. The interest shown and help afforded by the Department of Agriculture for Scotland and the Crofters Commission has helped to make the scheme a success. Mr Jimmy Dean gave invaluable help and advice, the scheme had the welcome co-operation of the Crofters Commission and the local press, too, assisted in arousing attention and encouragement because it was needed. Not everyone welcomed this. It meant that the Stud Book was taking more interest; it meant that some of the buyers could no longer persuade the owners of foals that there was no trade or demand; it meant, in fact, that these crofter owners were made aware that more people than they thought might be interested in their ponies.

The Department gave the Stud Book Society an annual grant towards this scheme and the balance of expenditure was met by the Betting Levy Board grant. Now it appears that the premiums paid to the stallion owners were ridiculously small – just £20. It is true, however, that the stallions were insured and no travelling or transport charges had to be paid by owners so this same rate of premium was paid for several years. Then the difficulty of procuring ponies good enough for the work enforced the Society to raise the amount. It has always been hard to find sufficient good stallions for the scheme and present prices and charges for service fees make it even more difficult. Stallions are available but many of those offered are not of sufficiently good breeding to improve the quality of the foals they sire. The scheme has often proved that unless a stallion has the necessary breeding and blood behind him, the odds are that 90% of his foals will be very ordinary. There have only been one or two exceptions to this rule. It is a difficult problem for those who run the

*33*

scheme to find enough good quality stallions to accept for the season. There are too many indifferent stallions, not only in conformation but also without essential breeding and sound blood lines.

There is alas, one salient point which a few of the pony breeders in Shetland have failed to grasp or have chosen to ignore. From the beginning of the stallion scheme it was emphasised that its aim and object was to improve the quality not the quantity of ponies in the Shetland Isles. This was not to prevent a breeder running as many mares as in previous years or to suggest that a scattald should hold fewer mares than would warrant a stallion being placed there, but it was hoped that the number of breeding mares would not be vastly increased. Actually, the number of mares did not show any great upward trend until about 1969 or 1970, when, due to the tremendously good trade at sales in those years, some breeders decided that it would pay them better to keep another mare or two and fewer sheep. Outside the scheme, also, there was a large increase in mares not owned by shareholders but by those who kept them on their own farms or enclosures, as elsewhere in the British Isles.

It is debatable as to how much longer the Premium Stallion Scheme can continue in its present form. It depends on the economic state of the country, whether home and export markets remain open for so many ponies and whether the present grants will continue, even if they are not increased. However, it does seem that the greatly increased number of privately owned entires in the islands, which are not all used exclusively for the owners' mares, might make it possible to reduce the number of Premium stallions without seriously affecting successful breeding of ponies in the northern isles.

Another influential factor concerning the possible reduction in number of stallions granted premiums is the limiting of grazing ground because of apportionments being granted to shareholders by the Crofter Commission. A shareholder of a scattald or common grazing may apply to the Commission for an apportionment of land. After taking various matters into consideration, as well as possible objections from other shareholders, the applicant is given permission to fence in an allotted amount of land on a strictly defined part of the common grazing. A generous grant is given towards the cost of fencing. Naturally enough these enclosures are made on the most accessible and possibly better land. On some grazings, therefore, where there have been made a number of apportionments, the stock left on the open scattald must find what keep they can – often only the poorer and more heathery parts of the grazing, or along the roads between the fences. This 'between fence' grazing is undesirable as it exposes ponies, and sheep as well, to the danger of passing motor traffic. In recent years there have been some unfortunate accidents where animals have been killed or maimed. However, if there is better grazing on the roadside verges it is only natural for stock to find its way there, and unfortunately where a road is remade or straightened the newly-sown verge is fertilized so that there is a quicker and better take of grass seed.

If the mares are to have access to the Premium stallions it is necessary for them to be on the hill. It would be unwise and unsafe to have them inside a wire fence with a stallion on the other side.

During the early years of this century there were a few influential studs in the islands, but most of the ponies were crofter owned. Many descendants of these crofter owners still keep ponies and frequently mares can be traced back to ponies in the possession of their forebears. It is interesting to be able to discern, in a number of cases, a distinct family resemblance amongst the ponies owned by a crofter breeder even though his neighbours may have ponies of a slightly different type.

It must be remembered that when the Stud Book Society began and for at least the succeeding twenty-five years, the pony was in many cases an economic necessity for the crofter. Apart from the small return he may have received for the sale of a foal or two he naturally wanted a pony that was as useful to him as possible and one that also might possibly give him a better financial return, although that was more of a pious hope than a reality.

Today the Annual Foal Sales are two important events for pony breeders in Shetland and interest is always shown by many who do not own ponies. These sales were started in 1958 as a means to enable crofters and others to receive prices near the market price which, previous to this, had not always been the case. All sorts of incidents and adventures have happened to some of the spectators and buyers who come up from the south. When trade is buoyant there is a great spirit of well-being and even if the weather is cold and stormy it does not matter. During the last seventy or eighty years one or two writers on ponies have written of new or special 'breeds' in Shetland, but these attempts at crossbreeding were usually local and shortlived. Edmonston, as already quoted, mentions that ponies of other breeds were introduced but, owing to the severity of the conditions, these did not contribute in any way to the Shetland pony breed.

In 1837 Sir Arthur Nicholson introduced into Fetlar an Arab stallion. He was called a 'mustang' and has been mentioned by more than one author as the originator of what was called the 'Fetlar pony'. Doubtless this entire (and probably a successor) were used in Fetlar but it seems likely that he was used exclusively on his owner's mares. The laird owned a large amount of land with a number of well fenced, high walled enclosures and it is not at all likely that any crofter owned mares had access to this Arab. Furthermore the laird would have had suitable buildings to house this stallion and his half bred progeny during the worst weather. Although Fetlar is a fertile island there is not everywhere a great deal of natural shelter and it is highly unlikely that any half or three-part bred Arab could survive the conditions which a pure Shetland pony could endure.

There is now no trace of this Arab blood in Fetlar. Although there have quite recently been at least two references to the so called 'Fetlar pony' it would be difficult if not impossible to produce authoritative and convincing evidence of their existence. If anyone can delineate this 'breed', no stallion on the island could possibly be classified as such nor has there been such an animal for at least fifteen years if not more.

Unfortunately the Department of Agriculture arranged more recently for a Highland pony stallion to be placed on the island. The purpose of this move was to have a larger pony for work on crofts and to carry larger loads of peat for the peat banks in Fetlar are a distance from most dwellings. Until a few years ago there were a number of half-bred garrons – plain ponies of about 12–13 h.h., but they were little used. Their most recent function was probably to round up the Shetland ponies when the foals were to be weaned. Now it is unlikely that any remain and probably all ponies on Fetlar are pure Shetland.

In 1903 Sir Walter Gilby wrote of a 'Sumburgh' breed of pony which was reputed to be a cross between a Norwegian stallion imported in the middle of the last century and Shetland mares. It is certain that larger stallions were introduced by the proprietor of the Sumburgh estates: quite probably one or more may have been Norwegian. John 'Sheepy' Smith remembered some of these around Sand Lodge at the beginning of the present century and he stated that they were mostly black or brown with white hind feet. He also confirmed that the stallion, possibly by then a crossbred, was kept entirely for the use of the working pony mares which were larger than the Shetland.

Writing in 1913 of the ponies in the Shetland Isles as he found them, Charles Douglas states 'The chief defect of the island ponies are to be found in the movement and conformation of the hocks – "cow hocks" being common and a tendency to excessive bending of the joints'. He mentions that this gives a look of 'curbiness' to the hock, although he stresses that actual curbs are very rare as are most other unsoundnesses. He considers that it is the undue hardship in early life which causes this poor hind leg in so many ponies and the roach backs also. It is true that a badly reared young pony is liable to show exaggeration of any defects in limbs, joints or conformation: unfortunately, however, there are many ponies, elsewhere, not only in Shetland, with poor hind legs and mean, stiff and weak hocks. It is confirmed by Douglas that these defects were present sixty years ago, and endorsement is provided by photographs taken twenty to thirty years earlier. Unfortunately not all the stallions then or now have good hind legs so this fault has not been corrected as it might. The heads of some island ponies show a tendency to plainness which is a great pity for the Shetland can and should have a well-shaped neat head, prominent eyes and small ears, and not the long, 'coffin' shaped head which is sometimes seen.

It is true that some ponies lack sufficient bone but it must be remembered that many animals in Shetland are of necessity bred on poor acid land and unless they have easy access to seaweed cannot procure a sufficient intake of minerals for good growth and bone structure. There are a few narrow seams of limestone running approximately north and south through the eastern side of the

Shetland pony and foal

islands and ponies and other stock reared and fed on this ground without doubt do benefit greatly.

A visitor to the islands will notice that many of the adult ponies are
inclined to be 'gutty' or carry a belly and that some old mares,
although suckling a foal, appear to be still carrying one. This is due
to the fact that so much of the grazing on which they run is very fibrous
and their intake of food is necessarily far greater than it would be for
ponies running on reasonably good grazing. Young mares will lose
these pronounced bellies on being moved to normal grass, but the
old 'ladies' alter little. Even a stallion running on the scattald for a
season will come off in autumn with a 'gutty' look. It will also be
noticed that ponies on such land graze over a much longer period of
the day than they would on a normal pasture: this is necessary so that
they may have a large enough intake from which to derive sufficient
nourishment.

*38*

Considering the available grazing, it is really remarkable how the mares produce the milk required to successfully rear a foal but this they most certainly do. It seems that all domestic animals in Shetland have a very high rate of conversion of available foodstuffs to milk; the native ewes produce much milk for their lambs and the now extinct Shetland cow was capable of a very long lactation on a low protein diet.

As is true of the Shetland sheep, all colours are to be found in the islands, but black ponies are probably the most common and skewbalds must come second. There are a fair number of browns and bays, which is unfortunately for some reason not a popular colour at present, a few piebalds and even fewer greys. The strong demand for chestnuts means that they have been favoured, but they are in part responsible for some of the worst of the bad hindlegged ponies, insufficient care having been taken to ensure that only good, sound chestnut stallions are used. Neither grey duns nor yellow duns are common. It appears that at one time more coloured ponies were in evidence but their popularity in the U.S.A. as well as at home meant that many ponies left the islands. Even so it has been said that in the early years of this century chestnuts and duns were quite frequently found in the west districts of Mainland. The 'Druid' writing in 1865 confirms the distribution to be much as it is now.

My wife and I have always tried to persuade members to see Shetland for it is the homeland of their breeding stock, but very few have ever thought of seeing for themselves the conditions and terrain in which ponies have to live – the rocky hills, the long heather clad slopes, the moss and lochs. Shetland has also interesting archaeological features and much of geological and historical importance.

Those who have not been to the Shetland Isles have no idea of the conditions in which these ponies are kept or of the land on which they live throughout the year. There is always shelter of some sort but in extreme weather which can smite the islands many would consider that the available protection is barely sufficient. Normally it is quite unusual for a pony to know what overhead shelter is, for it is seldom inside a building except for some special reason such as having its feet trimmed or being loaded for transport. During winter, particularly if it is hard, some supplementary feeding is given – possibly a sheaf of corn, a few potatoes or hay. The mention of the trimming of feet suggests possibly a visit from a farrier, but there is no longer such a tradesman in the islands and all trimming of feet is done by the owner or neighbour. It is unfortunately true that not as much care of feet is undertaken as is desirable, yet by and large few ponies are seen with badly neglected hooves.

Some mares do become fairly lean before the spring growth appears and there is no doubt that foals are occasionally cast or aborted due to the mare's low condition. This is not always so, however, and some foals are cast during spells of frost when the water supplies of a small burn or loch are frozen so that it is hard to find drinking water. Some times, though less often than in the past, one sees a mare on a hill followed by her yearling daughter as well as her newly dropped foal: the yearling will not still be allowed to suck, but the fact that the mare has been suckling it all winter and carrying her foal also can scarcely enable her to remain in good condition.

It is extraordinary how tales of woes and hardship, although they may be imaginary, always seem to be repeated more often than tales of happiness and comfort, particularly when animals are the chief subject. This is true in the case of the stories about how wretched ponies would starve had they not got seaweed to consume during the winter months. Ponies do eat or browse on seaweed in Shetland where they have access to the shore and they do this in spring, summer and winter, but not every pony has access and much of the shore is not suitable for ponies to walk on. Obviously they relish seaweed and it must supply them with traces of various minerals which would not otherwise be available to them. Possibly many years ago when the pony population was very high more sea-ware was eaten than today because the numbers were greater and it may have been more difficult to find sufficient food. On the other hand, sheep numbers were considerably less than in more recent years. Sheep, too, regularly go to the ebb where access is readily gained.

One knowledgeable breeder in Shetland discussing the splendid condition of some yearling fillies which had had access to seaweed on the shore since birth, asserted that this was the reason these fillies had done so well. He has two separate holdings, one of which has no access to the ebb but is possibly better land than the other which has, however, a long stretch of shore. The young stock from the former never do as well as those on the latter so in fact he often brings young ponies to this holding from the first, to enable them to browse on the sea-ware.

Strange as it may appear it seems an established fact that Shetland foals, if they are wintered on reasonable ground and not left on the hill with their dam, will be more mature than their counterparts in Scotland or England unless the latter have done exceptionally well. Most eighteen month old fillies bred and reared in Shetland are much more mature than those further south and might easily be taken for two year olds.

Yearling fillies are sometimes run on the scattalds of necessity and have the opportunity of being served by a stallion there. One does now and again hear of or see a two year old foaling, but this is not general. Most fillies foal at three years old and one seldom hears of their having trouble or difficulty which is possibly due to their early maturity and lean, fair condition. However quite a few of these fillies foaling at three fail to conceive that spring and the second foal may not arrive until they are five or rising five.

# 4

# *Breeding*

A dictionary definition of breeding is to 'produce offspring' and this of course is the general broad meaning when we talk of the breeding of animals, whether rabbits, sheep or Shetland ponies. There is no differentiation here between the schoolboy who has a cage of white mice which produce young with monotonous regularity and the wealthy owner of classical thoroughbreds: they are both, in the broader sense, breeders. But what a wealth of difference there is! One merely keeps a male animal with females of the same species, there is less selection than there is even in the wild, and it is the most powerful, cunning male who will mate with females of his selection; the other chooses selected females and mates them to a sire whose attributes are those most likely to influence the progeny in every beneficial way. Between these two examples lie a myriad others. Here, however, we are concerned with the shaping of a policy of improvement of ponies through a sensible, methodical and proved pattern.

A certain breed society secretary when talking about his society, its members and the animals they bred remarked, 'We have nearly 2000 members in our society but only twenty-five breeders'. This was his way of expressing the fact that only a small fraction of members were striving continually to breed the very best of that particular breed of animal and to improve all their stock; others were merely trying to produce one or two outstanding specimens for shows, and the remaining members were content to ensure that their breeding stock continued to produce pure-bred progeny which were probably no improvement on the parents.

This, alas, is often the case. For a long time many breeders of varying livestock have only bothered to increase, not improve their stock. There are even members of the Shetland Pony Stud Book Society who can be classified in this category. Surely an owner of ponies who breeds a foal or two each year should ask himself the question: 'Am I trying to produce better foals?' From some it is certain that a truthful answer would be 'No', because every year the same stallion is used on the same mares although the foals produced are not very useful. If an individual wants to keep a pony (or any other animal) purely as a pet he should do so, but these pets should be of the same sex so that none are bred. When replacements are required in due course then they should come from a reputable breeder. Every owner of Shetland ponies should consider seriously into which category he falls and then decide whether to breed: he should choose between improving the progeny or remaining as a pet owner and ceasing trying to propagate the breed.

The science of breeding animals up to a high standard is fascinating. It cannot be learnt in a short time, or by reading the odd book or two, or by listening to a few chance remarks: it can be learnt only through experience which is backed up by discussion with those more experienced and the digestion of appropriate written matter on the subject. Many things must be considered, many difficulties may arise, but if the efforts are successful they lead to much pleasure and satisfaction. Even the most successful breeder however, is rarely entirely satisfied and he will crave to achieve even better results.

There are ponies, as well as other animals, which will never produce progeny likely to be an improvement on themselves. This is particularly true of some stallions, so if the owner's aim (as one hopes) is to improve his stock, it is a waste of time, effort and money to continue using such an animal. It may be difficult, both sentimentally and physically, to get rid of some such pony, but a genuine intention to improve one's ponies necessitates a hardening of heart. Major contributions to successful breeding of improved stock are discrimination, elimination and selective acquisition.

If an owner's mares are reasonably good, without extremes, and a really well-bred stallion is acquired which also has the best points of a reputable Shetland pony, then there is some chance that the progeny may be superior to the mares. However, if the mares are all shapes and sizes it is unlikely that all the foals will be improved.

Owners should, not only to improve progeny but surely, also, for aesthetic reasons, have mares similar in appearance. Unless the stud has been in existence for some years or the owner has succeeded in buying a number of mares from one stud it is unlikely that the resemblance will be pronounced, but there is no reason why the type should not be similar. The secretary of the breed society quoted earlier in this chapter was visiting several studs. At one where he was taken into a field where six or eight mares were grazing, he looked round quickly but with discernment; then, turning to his companion, he said, 'This is a breeder's stud, and I mean BREEDER's with capital letters'. The meaning is clear: here was a bunch of mares obviously bred with care, all of a similar, good type showing definite characteristics.

It has often been correctly said that the stallion is more than half the herd, yet time and again this is ignored. Stallions are used which not only have bad faults in their conformation and lack breed character but which have virtually no breeding or pedigree behind them at all. Is it surprising that one hears owners remarking that such and such a stallion has not left any good foals? Is it surprising that so many of the foals one sees at shows are poor? It is impossible that a badly made, thick shouldered, heavy headed pony with no breeding behind him can be expected to improve stock unless the mares to which he has been bred are even worse.

We often see in stallion classes animals of the poorest conformation, narrow, with bad action and sickle hocks, or common sorts with round coarse bone. These ponies are not good enough to be used as stallions. Moreover, they are often of no sound breeding, stallions that are ever likely to be heterozygous.

One may well ask why do we have stud books and pedigree ponies if we do not make full use of these? Why must colts and stallions of poor or indifferent breeding and bloodlines be used when colts and stallions of proven bloodlines and of first class breeding are available?

Regrettably, one of the reasons is that their colour is often wrong! Another reason is sentimentality. Unfortunately, if owners are prepared to put certain preference first their chances of continued success are bound to be reduced. They should, if they wish, breed coloured ponies, but ensure that the stallion is well made and has some known and respected bloodlines in his pedigree. If they have to part with a colt or stallion they are particularly fond of, but who is of little or no value for breeding, one of two easy alternatives can be chosen. If by making a change it means that ponies and breed can be improved, a stallion can be gelded or painlessly destroyed – both options are far more honest and humane than passing him on as an entire to some unsuspecting person.

Where bloodlines are concerned, it used to be maintained, and probably still is, that the top lines of parents in a pedigree should both be from studs of well-known breeders. This ensured that the pony did at least have considerable breeding. There is a greatly enhanced possibility that such a stallion will be homozygous or prepotent and that in consequence his foals will be more akin to him in quality and type. In this respect it is astonishing how few breeders really study pedigrees and take an intelligent interest in the breeding of a pony. Stallions and colts of real breeding are admittedly not two a penny, and proven stallions still less so, but nevertheless top class colts or colt foals can be found which will almost certainly turn out first rate stallions. If colour is very important the solution is not so straightforward; however, the owner of coloured mares should not accept any stallion because he is the desired colour, but rather find a sufficiently good entire which may not be exactly the right colour. There is no doubt that in recent years many coloured stallions have changed hands purely because of their colour, and prices for them have been much higher than their value for the breeding of good foals. This is a situation which is directly opposed to any standard practice of good breeding.

Breeding for particular points or colours in animals merely to satisfy the whims of some breeders, or for show, has done more damage to various breeds of domestic animals than is generally recognised. Many show points can be most injurious to a breed and it is ill-advised to underline some exaggerated and unnatural points. It would be out of place to list all these absurd, widespread characteristics in various animals which have been developed purely for show fashion: examples are certain breeds of dogs which have grave unsoundnesses amounting to lethal factors; breeds of sheep which, owing to the development of large heads because these are considered an asset in the show ring, have serious trouble lambing; cattle which have been bred too small for economical commercial use, and others which produce insufficient milk to feed their calves: pigeons which owing to conformation, are unable to feed their young. These points have been developed because of competition in the show ring. It is too easy to say that this could never happen to the Shetland pony and people probably said that about some of the faults mentioned above. But these faults can materialise from the exaggeration of some quite minor point of conformation stressed by one or two exhibitors. No breed remains exactly the same from one generation to another and the fashion for Shetland ponies that are awarded prizes in the shows changes from time to time. Over a period of a few years there is a pronounced difference of type in many of the ponies exhibited.

I have mentioned elsewhere changes in fashion in the show rings. When we started exhibiting, the favoured pony was a quality one with neat head, a really good neck and shoulder, free moving, most definitely a pony. For some reason the ponies put up became heavier, larger and more like a draught type. I am aware that some breeders of Shetland ponies will not agree with me but no one can deny that this pony has always been primarily a pack or riding animal and the short phase in its history when it was used and bred for draught by a small proportion of breeders is insignificant. Its role is that of a useful pony with good quality characteristics, a pony that can cover rocky, mossy or steep ground with ease or can stride self-assuredly along a road to a gig or dogcart. A strange and curious feature of this change is that it came when the demand for pit ponies had already been in existence for almost seventy of its 100 years. It seems that it was not the pit pony that some breeders had in mind but rather that they were endeavouring to create the impression that the Shetland should be a small edition of the Clydesdale. This is certainly an erroneous, prejudiced opinion, and one that has only been held by a handful; but they have persuaded more to adopt their belief.

In another chapter I have already quoted the well-known breeders of the past as R.W.R. MacKenzie and Charles Douglas who stressed in writing that the Shetland was not a draught animal. I have heard the late Lady Estella Hope emphasise this also, as have other authorities such as Professor Bryner Jones who was an expert on all farm animals. All writers and recorders of the past, whether knowledgeable of a pony's conformation or not, give descriptions of ponies being ridden, carrying goods and produce on their backs, but never drawing anything except a light gig or road vehicle. However, by no means all breeders or judges were influenced by this or other changes of fashion and they have continued to breed the type of pony which they consider to be nearest to the best type of Shetland pony. There can be seen throughout the islands in Shetland today some splendid ponies by any standard. They may be too light of bone or may be over 42″, but they are undoubtedly of Shetland origin and active, fair quality animals.

Recently the Stud Book Society Council decided to deprecate the use of the word 'miniature' with regard to smaller Shetlands or those under 34″. This was instigated through fear that some breeders of these ponies, (which have occurred in the breed for hundreds of years), might try to determine a special branch of the breed. It had, in fact, been mooted that there should be a special section for these smaller ponies in the Stud Book. The Council, mindful of what they had seen of miniature breeds and by no means impressed, decided against countenancing such a proposition.

In a previous chapter it was noted that well over 100 years ago the ministers in Unst were disturbed at the increase of the smallest ponies and that stallions of the 'most puny size' were allowed to go at large. It is an established fact that from time to time very small ponies have appeared; one saw occasionally a few together on a scattald in Shetland, and we are told authoritatively that in Unst, if not in other islands, there were always some diminutive ponies. Certainly there have always been some very small ponies in the breed and they do appear quite unexpectedly now and again in studs where the normal sized pony is bred. However, owners must surely realise that there can obviously be only a small demand for them for their use is strictly limited. The Shetland pony has always been a utility animal (or potentially so) except for these very small ones.

Many well-known breeders and judges in the past whilst admiring small types and, if good enough, placing them high in the ring, have expressed concern that the breeding of these might be carried on indiscriminately. The maximum height for a mature Shetland is 42″ but no minimum height was ever fixed, so a pony of any height within the limit must be fairly considered by a judge.

Charles Douglas firmly asserts that 'A height of more than 40 inches is properly regarded as a serious fault'. This, written in 1913, emphasises how show ring fashions change because not long after ponies exceeding 40″ were winning in the ring. He goes on, however, to say,

'On the other hand, there has, in recent years, been a tendency to undue diminution in size – the former desire of breeders to increase height having given place to a morbid ambition to produce pigmy ponies. It must be kept in mind that ponies of sizes less than 34 inches are of little use for practical purposes. Anything which tends to make the pony merely an oddity and a toy, and to take it out of the category of useful or usable horses, is fatal to the prospects of the breed and should be resisted by breeders and judges.'

In 1913, presumably during the National Pony Society's show which was held there for many years, there was a class for 'miniature' ponies at the Agricultural Hall. The height limit was eight hands and seven ponies were entered, the smallest being just six hands three inches.

As far as I am aware there is only one breeder in Shetland today actually concentrating on these very small ones though two or three stallions in the islands do not exceed 34″. It seems to me that there is too much sensational enthusiasm in the breeding of these very small ponies for the only possible use for these little ones is that of ornamental attraction. They can be used in harness but are really too small – except for some very special and rare pursuit – and the market for them could very soon be satiated. Efforts to breed them smaller and even smaller are disturbing: this is an alarming trend which I understand has followers in countries other than ours. What I consider to be a very great danger is the breeding of thoroughly bad little ones: it must be put on record that there are quite a number of miserable little weeds, short of bone, with poor heads, badly made and with weak action. These should be of no value to anyone, but unfortunately both for the breed and for themselves are reproducing their own kind. On the other hand there are some splendid examples of excellent conformation and action amongst these wee ones and many have an even better temperament than some of the larger, more ordinarily sized ponies.

The importance of using a top class stallion has already been stressed. It is astonishing how many newcomers to the breed or to pony breeding, will buy expensive mares but grudge spending money on a stallion and often choose some indifferent colt for their stud horse. It should be remembered that established breeders have reached their status by producing good ponies and that it is more likely that their colts or stallions will produce good quality foals than one with a mixed, short and doubtful pedigree. It is, of course, not always prizewinners which make the best sires and novices are warned against expecting that a stallion who has excelled in shows will necessarily breed well; for it may be found that a stallion which is not a top class show pony may well breed extremely well. It is worthwhile for an intending purchaser of a stud pony to visit the pony's sire and dam and possibly other relations also, or if it is a stallion that has been in use, to see some of his get.

The Shetland pony, today, traces back through the years to comparatively few ponies. There are consequently a considerable amount of fairly close relationships, though now in most cases it would be necessary to trace the relationship back beyond the sixth or seventh generation. Even ponies with short pedigrees are often related to some with a few generations in the Stud Book. It has been particularly so in the case of ponies in the islands: they are pure bred but their progenitors have not been registered for some generations.

The popularity of the Londonderry strains, particularly during the first twenty years of this century, was understandable, for breeders wished to maintain the improved bone and substance which had been developed by this stud. However, some prominent breeders of this period also felt that concentration on these bloodlines could be too pronounced and they sought other sources of sound, fresh strains. Charles Douglas undoubtedly had considerable admiration for some of the improvements made by Lord Londonderry's stud managers yet he did not seem to be convinced that breeders should be contented. He stressed the value and importance of the combination of Odin and Prince of Thule blood, yet had this to say,

> 'But he ought not to make this his only source. The islands still contain animals and strains well fitted to be a strength to the breed; and one of the most interesting parts of a breeder's work consists in the careful and gradual introduction of these outside strains of blood'.

This advice is still undoubtedly valid today, but naturally some preliminary research and observation are necessary. Many inexperienced breeders select a stallion after only a brief look, without scrutinising the pedigree or examining prospects from the records of forebears and of other progeny.

The breeder must clearly visualise the ultimate result of his efforts and should not deviate from this aim. Unless there is pre-eminent purpose in breeding only great luck or chance can forestall failure.

A stallion of close or line breeding, (provided that these lines are free of genes which might cause serious faults or imperfections) is far more likely to be prepotent and his progeny homogenetic, than an entire whose sire's lines are entirely different from those of his dam. A pony of outcross breeding may sire some very good foals but many may inherit the worst faults of both sire and dam.

Should an outcross bred stallion be used, it is strongly urged that this is not done indiscriminately and his progeny should be bred back to the original lines. The use of an outcross sire may cause great variability in offspring which is definitely a disadvantage to the owner who is trying to establish or keep to a definite family type. If, however, the sole object is to breed a show winner – in other words an individual – then purity of line is no advantage.

Numerous awards at shows may have been gained by a stallion of exceptionally fine conformation, but he may be heterozygous to import genes and will only pass one half of this to his progeny. The selection of a suitable stallion is difficult enough but if colour has to be considered also, the choice is greatly narrowed down and much harder to make. It is amazing how comparative novices attempt to breed something particular which experienced breeders might think about more than twice.

There is danger in breeding merely for some fashionable point or other. Hagedoorn stated 'The purification of breeds by in-breeding defeats its own ends when the *breeding of show animals is concerned*, for as soon as some quality is fixed in the breed it may become out-moded'. This is as true for Shetland ponies as for fancy rabbits or pigeons.

Though little has yet been said about mares they are, of course, highly important as well as absolutely necessary!

The new breeder should, if possible, try to find mares that are of approximately the same type, as this eventually will greatly help the quicker formation of a stud type. If there is a choice, looking at previous foals or other relations helps point out the possible result of mating, and if one can also see the sire of her progeny this, too, will give an idea of the mare's breeding potential. The buyer is strongly advised not to buy a mare with a glaring structural fault or a doubtful breeding record. As in the case of stallions it is not always the prize-winning mares which make the best breeders – rather it is those who have good breeding behind them. Their pedigree should be considered as well as their conformation, and although some short pedigree mares of good background are as pure and have as good bloodlines as many with six generations in the Stud Book, these unfortunately cannot be discovered.

In 1972 the Shetland Pony Stud Book Society, which had been concerned for some time about the poor quality of some stallions being registered, brought in a Stallion Inspection Scheme for England and Wales. Scotland, at that time, was in a slightly different position, for the Department of Agriculture sent one of their livestock inspectors with the examining veterinary surgeon to ensure that the pony being examined for a stallion licence was of true breed type and character. In the same year, however, the Department decided that this inspection could not be continued and the Stud Book Society's scheme was extended to include Scotland the following spring. Although the scheme is not ideal it does at least ensure that the worst of the ponies submitted are not accepted: it may also make owners consider their colts more carefully before applying for an inspection.

Briefly, the scheme is as follows: Any owner who wishes to register a two year or older colt as a stallion in the Stud Book must apply to the Secretary early in the year and at the same time deposit a fee. In due course an appointment is made for an inspection by two members of the judges' panel, who, having examined the pony for type and character, pass their decision to the Secretary. If the colt is accepted the owner may then apply for a licence from the Department of Agriculture or the Ministry of Agriculture according to where he or she lives. On receiving the licence after veterinary examination, application is then made to the Society for registration.

There is no doubt whatsoever that such a scheme is a very necessary procedure as only a few veterinary surgeons are thoroughly conversant with the conformation, type and character of a Shetland pony. It is unfair to expect them to give a verdict on this as well as the soundness of the pony. Improvements may well be made to this initial scheme and no doubt the running of it will be continually under review, but at present its two major handicaps are finance and the availability of judges.

The scheme has aroused the interest of other pony breed societies and probably more than one of these societies will follow suit in the not too distant future.

It should be understood that the Society's stallion inspection is in no way veterinary. This is left to the vet who is appointed by the Ministry or Department to carry out the examination. Nevertheless, if the Society's judges observed some really bad fault – possibly in action due to faulty conformation – they would be justified in refusing to accept the colt for registration. It is the responsibility of the owners not to submit colts with obvious faults particularly those of an hereditary nature, for example, luxation of the patella or slipping stifle, ponies which go exceedingly wide behind, that dish badly and so on; nor should they submit either a colt with an overshot or undershot jaw, parrot-mouthed or swine-chopped.

To close this chapter I shall briefly discuss the make, shape and action of the Shetland pony which it is desirable to breed. As stated earlier two types developed, or it would be more correct to say that a second type was developed during the late nineteenth century for use in the pit trade and other draught work. It has already been made clear that the Shetland pony was, prior to 1870, purely a pony that was required for carrying goods or persons on its back, and surely the pony required today is similar. It is a pony that should show quality, with a pony head and small ears; it should have well defined nasal cavities, a large and prominent eye and a broad muzzle. This head should be carried well on a graceful neck, not crested unless a stallion, coming from a well laid or sloped shoulder; this shoulder must be distinct and the withers reasonably prominent. The ribs should be well sprung and deep, but the barrel should not be too sprung or round, otherwise it will restrict the movement of the shoulder. The quarters should be strong and powerful and the tail well set on. The second thighs should be well developed. The limbs should have sufficient bone which must be flat – quality bone not round and coarse. The knees should be flat, fairly prominent and not too far off the ground; with a reasonably short cannon bone, the pastern sloping but not long and weak, the fetlock joint clean and well defined.

In the hindleg the hock joints must be fairly prominent and quite distinct and clean. The hindleg should not be hooky or sickle-hocked, and the cannon bone, pastern and fetlock joint should be as in the forelegs. The feet should be open and round with tough horn.

In action the pony should move all four limbs absolutely straight neither too close together or wide, with round action, but not extravagantly so, which covers the ground. A Shetland pony should have clean, muscular limbs, and must display activity.

The mane and tail should be abundant and of strong, straight hair which is not frizzy or crinkly. There should be some feather on the fetlock joints.

Black or any colour is acceptable.

The necessity for the large nasal cavities in the Shetland pony is oecological. Owing to their islands of origin being in northern latitudes, more than 60° nearer to the Arctic Circle than to the Isle of Wight, the air breathed is normally considerably colder than that in a more southern climate. Consequently nature has ensured that through these large nasal cavities the air is warmed before entering the lungs. The Arab horse, on the other hand, which originates from a warm country, does not require nor possess these large cavities.

It does appear sometimes that beginner breeders, although they may have had considerable experience with other ponies or horses, are prone to start their stud without properly studying the breed. They buy either an ill-selected bunch of mares or pick up here and there mares or fillies which have no affinity to the same type. When one is laying out a fair sum of money on a hobby or occupation which one hopes will be a long term one, it is worth spending time, a little more cash and having a thorough look at some of the well-established breeders' studs. This may be a saving in the end. It is quite probable that a selection of mares and fillies can be secured more cheaply and give the new owner greater satisfaction. Good ponies are, of course, quite often for sale by small, new breeders and suitable ponies may be found this way; but no-one without some knowledge of the breed should buy until he can differentiate between a good pony and an indifferent or bad one, or find someone who can give honest, skilled advice.

There is too much superficial judging of ponies and detail can be sadly ignored. Nowadays it seems expert knowledge is very readily absorbed and equally readily devolved.

Shetland stallion

# 5

# *Studs*

The Shetland Pony Stud Book was formed in 1890. Included amongst the entries in the first volume are ponies which belonged to owners living outside Shetland who had formed studs a number of years previously. These studs outside Shetland had been formed to breed ponies for the coal pits and more than one was situated in the north-east of England where the greatest demand was for the small pit pony.

The largest and most influential of these was that owned by the Marquis of Londonderry. His main stud farm was rented on the island of Bressay, an island lying off the east of Shetland Mainland opposite Lerwick. The manager had, in 1870 or shortly after, bought ponies from all over the islands which were as near as possible to those required for the mines. The males, except the very best, were sent south to County Durham whilst the mares and colts remained in Bressay. The aim was to breed a pony with as much weight near the ground as possible: to produce a small, heavy animal, able to pull a well laden tub through low seams. As the true Shetland pony had not been bred to pull, but to carry on its back a reasonable load, it would appear that not many of the sort wanted were available, particularly when one also takes into account the fact that other pit owners were trying to find these types and dealers from the U.S.A. hoped to collect sufficient quantities to ship over. We do know that some ponies of the required kind were found, probably more colts or stallions than mares, but of these stallions most of them figure fairly prominently in the start of the pedigrees of very many of the present day ponies.

Of these Jack 16 is the most famous. He is described as being 40″ high, close coupled with remarkable bone and substance and with upright carriage. He was of unknown parentage, nor in fact was his breeder known, but considering how well he bred it might be that he was closely or line bred, probably inadvertently. Jack had no less than forty-nine daughters, granddaughters or great granddaughters listed in Volumes I and II of the Stud Book. In addition he had three sons who were much used in this stud: Laird of Noss 20, Lord of the Isles 26 and Odin 32. Prince of Thule 36 was for using on these mares, though not entirely, as close breeding was at times used. In his excellent analysis of the breeding policies of the Londonderry stud, Charles Douglas tells us that Prince of Thule 36 was of exquisite quality, there being a tendency to largish heads and low head carriage. Douglas considered that this influence might not have lasting effect. If, however, Prince of Thule himself did not have this lasting influence it is certain that his son Oman 33 had very considerable impact on the ponies of that period both in the Londonderry stud and after its dispersal. He was said to be a compact, massive, dark brown pony of 35″. His dam was Norna 198, a grand daughter of Jack 16.

Of Jack's sons Odin 32 was probably the most influential. This is at least partly because he was used more than Laird of Noss 20 in the stud and he was the only one of the three to continue in use after the dispersal. Lord of the Isles 26 had been exported to the U.S.A. and Laird of Noss 20 was not included in the sale nor does there appear to be any note of his export, so probably he died before the stud was dispersed.

Odin 32 had sired 119 foals in the stud before the sale, when he was bought by the Ladies E. and D. Hope. He is described as being a powerful, masculine pony but his head was rather too big. Probably one of the most successful sires from this stud, other than his grandsire, Jack 16, was Thor 83, by Odin 32 out of Fra 185 who was by Prince of Thule 36 out of a mare Hethe by Jack 16. Thor 83 apparently inherited his sire's heavy head and he, also, was a pony of great substance and a very free mover.

In most established and successful studs or herds the females trace back to a very limited number of mares – the tail females. So it was here and the five which are in the original Stud Book occur in many of the pedigrees of present day ponies – Darling 174, 39″ black mare; her sister Dumple 179, a brown of the same height, by Jack 16 out of Dandy; Spencie 209, another 39″ brown, by Jack 16 out of Seivwright; the already mentioned Fra 185; and Thora 212 a 36″ black by Odin 32 out of Thordisa – thus she had Jack 16 as paternal grandfather and again twice as maternal great grandfather. In addition to the stud in Shetland, where incidentally mare owners were able to use at least a few of the Londonderry sires, one was maintained at Seaham, Co. Durham.

On 7 September 1899 the Londonderry stud was sold by public auction at Seaham Harbour by Messrs Crow. This was an extremely important event in the history of the Shetland pony, as although draught sales had been held from time to time previously this was the complete dispersal of the stud. The prospective buyers were entertained to luncheon in marquees, toasts were proposed and drunk and bids might have come more freely as a result; but when one compares the general run of prices with what we are told were the normal run of commercial prices at that time, one comes to the conclusion that there must have been some useful bargains. 151 ponies were sold and the top price was 125 guineas for a three year old filly. The Ladies E. and D. Hope paid second top price for the three year old filly Sea Serpent, and secured the mare Bretta 811 for sixty guineas, at which price, also, Mrs Wentworth Hope Johnstone bought the two year old filly, Belinda. Otherwise very few rose above thirty guineas and the price of one or two of the colt foals was in single figures only; the now rising eighteen year old mare Fra 185 to whom so many ponies may be traced went to a Cumberland man for only twenty-one guineas. Thus this famous stud came to an end and D. McAdie, who devoted his life to ponies and had come from Caithness to take charge of the ponies on Bressay, moved to take charge of the stud of Mrs Bruce of Sumburgh.

There is no doubt that the Londonderry stud had a profound influence on the Shetland pony although this influence has been over-estimated both in value and numbers. Often one hears that such and such a stud is full of Londonderry blood, strain or type, but it is doubtful that there is now any real influence from that source. In fact, (although some might think this is heresy) do we want the modern Shetland pony – that is the pony which was similar in type to its ancestors before the pit trade started – to be like the pony which was striven for by the managers of the Londonderry stud? This would be a pony low to the ground, with low head carriage and straight shoulder, not a pony to carry a child, or even a pack, nor to trot smartly to a light gig.

It is undeniable, however, that this stud did much good: it selected the best ponies that could be found in the islands and bred carefully and selectively with them. In so doing it developed a stronger and better built animal. For the ponies in the islands had suffered as a result of the heavy demand for the best and left the poorer sorts to perpetuate their stock: this was pointed out by the ministers and Dr Edmonston in their reports.

Luckily, about half a dozen breeders of Shetlands, who were to make good use of their purchases in the immediate future, attended the sale. However a great deal of good blood was lost to the Shetland pony world, many ponies being lost to the breed at once, although the Ladies E. and D. Hope, R.W.R. MacKenzie, Anderson Manson, William Mungall, Francis Gourlay and H. F. Anderton all made purchases whose influence on the breed was generally impressive.

At about this time interest in Shetlands was increasing and a number of new studs were being formed. As has always been the case, however, a fair proportion of these were shortlived: the owners for various reasons decided not to carry on or were stopped by force of circumstance. Often in the changing of ownership some good ponies disappear from the Stud Book registrations: this probably accounts for the virtual disappearance of some Londonderry stock.

The late nineteenth century was a period of considerable prosperity. The internal combustion engine had not yet taken over road transport so ponies and horses were needed for transport as well as for numerous tasks on estates and in large gardens. There was no shortage of labour to attend to them. The owner of the motor car probably owned at least one or two horse or pony vehicles for pleasure or the more mundane work of carrying luggage and parcels to or from the station and shops. The Shetland pony was naturally popular for children to

Nineteenth century basket pony phaeton

drive as well as ride. Many were in double harness to a park phaeton, driven perhaps by their lady owner with a small sized groom on the rumble or, in the case of very light vehicles, riding sedately behind but ready at an instant to dismount and get to the heads of the pair. Queen Victoria used such a vehicle in Windsor Park.

One of the earliest studs, which is still flourishing today, was formed by the Ladies Estella and Dorothea Hope, daughters of the sixth Earl of Hopetoun. When children they had been given Shetland ponies from a drove from the islands landed at Leith, and they continued to keep them, later forming a stud when they moved to Sussex on the occasion of their brother's marriage. The Ladies Hope were original members of the Society and also very successful breeders who gained numerous awards in the shows over a long period. It appears that they had always a farseeing and constructive policy of breeding ponies: they bred closely and were particular that their stock was sound and of the best quality. As already noted they became the owners of Odin 32 to replace Prince of Thule 36 whom they had bought eight years earlier and had died after a fight with his son Oman 33. These three horses all had considerable influence in their stud and Odin 32 sired the mare Corona 2015 to whom many of the South Park ponies trace, from Hoplemuroma 130, a $35\frac{1}{2}''$ mare of unknown breeding in Shetland. From Shetland also the stallion Haldor 270 was bought from H. F. Anderton of Vaila; he had bred him from sire and dam purchased from the Londonderry stud and he was very inbred to Jack 16. Haldor, only $32\frac{1}{2}''$, left some well-known sons and daughters. He was bought a few years later by R. W. R. MacKenzie whose stallions had been beaten into second and third places by him at the Royal Show. The stallion, Seaweed 333, who did so well for the Transy stud, was bred by the Ladies Hope in 1901 from the young mare Sea Serpent 1535 by Oman 33, which had been secured at Seaham Harbour for eighty guineas. William Mungall bought the mare from them with Seaweed, a foal at foot, for eighty-nine guineas. However, as well as buying stallions from Shetland, at least two or three were sold to go up there, the best known being Royal Blood 359, for which a few years later the owner Dr Bowie, Bixter, was offered £300. Possibly the best and most influential entire they bred was Thoreau 392: he was apparently an exceptionally well-made pony and a very true, free mover. Thoreau was sired by Odin 32, as was his dam, and through him and Lord of the Isles 26 was extremely closely bred to Jack 16. Thoreau was bred to their mares of which a number were also by Odin 32 and other related stallions. Thoreau was $38''$ and had a very successful show career winning gold, six silver medals, eighteen first prizes, two second and one third: amongst these were more than one award for harness classes.

Haldor 270 appears to be the last stallion brought into the stud from outside, and Lady Estella, who carried on the stud alone after the death of her sister in 1907, relied entirely on entires she had bred. A study of the pedigrees of her ponies reveals not only the close relationship amongst themselves but also to the original foundation ponies. It is sometimes thought that Lady Estella latterly only kept the small or very small ponies. This is incorrect: she did considerably reduce the number of large ones, and she did breed many coloured ponies but she also had blacks. In 1901–2 she was President of the Stud Book Society but did not in later years take any active part in the running of the Society. Blessed with unusually good health and a splendid, active memory, Lady Estella had a firm grasp of pedigrees and breeding and told many amusing and interesting tales about ponies and their owners. She died in 1959, aged ninety-two.

The Stud, which never used a suffix or prefix, is still at South Park under the ownership of her great niece Lady Joan Gore-Langton.

Another stud of which the owner was an original member of the society was at Uyeasound, Unst, the property of Alexander Sandison. The stud had been long established and little, if any, recourse to Londonderry blood was made, for home or locally bred stallions were used. Names of ponies which he bred can be found in a number of contemporary pedigrees. Later this stud was to be named as under the ownership of A. Sandison & Sons, but it was sold in the early 1920s. It can be assumed that this stud had quite a considerable influence on many of the ponies bred in Unst for it was the only stud or herd in that island of any size, over fifty of its ponies being registered in the first volume of the Stud Book. It is of interest to note that the majority of those registered were other colours than black; cream, dun and white are mentioned. Alexander Sandison was a member of the original Council. Mr Ian Sandison, a son, restarted a small herd in Unst and this is now the property of his son Dr Louis Sandison. Only a very faint trace of the old Sandison breeding is present, however, through a mare bred by Lady Estella Hope.

Apart from the many crofters who owned and bred ponies another large herd was that owned by the Bruces of Sumburgh. Mr John Bruce was on the first Council of the Society. It would be more correct to say that this proprietor had three herds or studs, one on Mousa, an island lying off Sand Lodge, one at Sumburgh and a third on Fair Isle. These ponies do not figure very prominently in the breeding of many ponies, but high class stallions appear to have been used and Lord Londonderry used a 36″ Sumburgh stallion, Lion 22.

The foals seem to have been sold to one of the large dealers and probably many eventually reached the U.S.A. By 1927 most of the stock had been dispersed and the present stud was reformed after the last war by Mr Robert H. W. Bruce of Sand Lodge. There is, however, one mare which was traced back to the original stock through some papers and records in possession of the Sand Lodge grieve, Mr Billy Bray; it was also found that as far back as 1880 the Mousa and Sumburgh ponies were small – 32–33″. The National Trust for Scotland now owns Fair Isle and only very recently have ponies been re-introduced there, through a tenant of the Trust.

Thor 83

Apart from the Londonderry ponies another prominent name in breeding is Manson and it frequently recurs in pedigrees as such. In the first volume no less than forty-six mares are entered by Anderson Manson and two stallions both bred incidentally by Alex. Sandison; however home bred stallions seem to be more favoured subsequently. At the Londonderry dispersal the stallion, Sigurd 137, by Lord of the Isles 26 out of an Odin 32 mare, was bought along with four others. This pony and the stallion, Chacma 290, whose dam, Bronte 1277, presumably in foal to Thor 83, was one of the purchases which were to be of immense value to him and are responsible for the heavy infusion of Londonderry blood. The stallion, Transy Superior 577, was registered in the name of Manson who bought this pure Londonderry pony from William Mungall. A number of Manson bred stallions figure in many present day pedigrees such as Pole Star 884, Bright Star of Maryfield 1045, Diamond Star 697, and Coram 810. In 1936 Peter Manson sold the last of his ponies, probably on relinquishing his tenancy of Maryfield farm. Although the Manson

A Shetland pony mare

ponies had very strong Londonderry bloodlines, many of the later Maryfield ponies were certainly not of the draught type: they had substance but also showed great quality and action. Peter Manson was an extremely good, though deliberate, judge of ponies and of Shetland cattle.

The Andersons at Hillswick, in the north of Shetland Mainland, had a thriving business with ponies. They were mainly interested in their export to North America. To this end they owned stallions which were placed on some of the hills for the use of mare owners and they bought the subsequent foals.

H. F. Anderton of Vaila formed a small stud on that island, which lies off the western coast at Walls, shortly after purchasing the estate. The mares were of Londonderry breeding as was his stallion, Duncan 147, the sire of Haldor and other good ponies. No entries from this stud were made in the Stud Book after 1926, as it was dispersed at about that date. Apparently the ponies were taken off Vaila and shipped down to Aberdeen for sale. It is related that in spite of the quality and breeding of the stud the average price they fetched in those depressed times was about £4 10s.

There were, of course, numerous other breeders in Shetland who registered their ponies but few are readily traceable in pedigrees of present day animals.

It was only four years after the founding of the Stud Book Society that R.W.R. MacKenzie registered three mares all bred by Alex. Sandison of Uyeasound; in subsequent volumes the Earlshall prefix becomes more and more prominent. He used, to start with, a Bressay bred stallion, Pineapple 135, and increased his stock with females purchased from Seaham Harbour. The Earlshall stud grew to be large and influential and at times there were up to thirty foaling mares. There was a definite Earlshall type of pony which had quality and a fine head, possibly generally a little lighter in bone than some of the other studs of that period, with good action from the well laid shoulders. MacKenzie was a strong protagonist for the active, general purpose pony and not a supporter of the heavy draught sort. Helmet of Earlshall 408, foaled in 1904, was possibly the most influential stallion of his own breeding, certainly in the earlier years of the stud. This stallion was sired by Rattler 210, a $35\frac{1}{2}''$ dark brown bred by Gavin Hadden, sired by Multum in Parvo 28. Rattler had undoubtedly a substantial effect on the successful formation of the Earlshall stud. Bravo of Earlshall 115, a black 36" pony, is another which figures fairly prominently in pedigrees; he was by Bandrol 635, a pony bred by Mrs Huband, sired by a Uyeasound stallion out of an Earlshall mare. Other entires which occur in pedigrees of ponies of Earlshall breeding are Brass Hat 1212 who was by Helmet of Earlshall 408 and Dollar Boy 1242, a $39\frac{1}{4}''$ black by Bravo of Earlshall, both bred by Francis Gourlay. MacKenzie bred quite a number of coloured ponies, in fact his was the only prominent stud at that time which did so. He bought the grey Gluss Norseman 759 from Magnus Blance in Shetland and also had grey Empire Day 539 bred by A. R. Tongue. Why Not of Earlshall 898, a son of the latter, was another extensively used grey pony. Emmillius of Earlshall 1121 can be traced in very many chestnut ponies of today. He was in fact by the brown Sammy of Liberton 947 who in turn was by a brown Auchlochan pony; his dam was a brown mare Sunday 2412.

'Bob' MacKenzie was a tremendous character, well-known, well-liked, and one of the few breeders of note who used to visit Shetland now and again. He always wore cloth or tweed suits of a special pattern: a short, square cut tail-coat from the pockets of which he would produce his snuff box and large, coloured handkerchief. He was always happy to give advice to those who were starting with Shetlands or to those who sought his counsel. If, however, anyone preferred not to be co-operative or was, in his opinion, not being as helpful as he might, he could be caustic and unflattering.

For eight or more years an annual sale of Shetland ponies was held at Earlshall. Other owners as well as R.W.R. MacKenzie entered ponies. Mares and stallions, colts, fillies and foals were all sold. Unfortunately no detailed records of these sales or catalogues seem to be in existence now, but the overall averages for ponies sold and the number of vendors between 1903 and 1911 are of interest.

|      | Number sold | Number of vendors | Average Price |
|------|-------------|-------------------|---------------|
| 1903 | 57          | 3                 | £16 13s 4d    |
| 1904 | 108         | 9                 | £15 4s 0d     |
| 1905 | 111         | 16                | £16 11s 0d    |
| 1907 | 86          | 10                | £19 8s 6d     |
| 1908 | 115         | 17                | £14 4s 3d     |
| 1909 | 90          | 14                | £23 2s 7d     |
| 1910 | 124         | —                 | £20 13s 2d    |
| 1911 | 106         | —                 | £17 18s 2d    |

For a few years before his death MacKenzie lived at Carpow in north-west Fife, having left Earlshall, and on 23 November 1932 he dispersed his well-known stud at Sunderland. It was during the depression and scarcely anyone was looking for ponies nor were they disposed to travel to Sunderland for this sale. So the top price for ponies from this famous herd was very low – 33 guineas for the well-known Dollar Boy 1242 and a four year old filly, Elderflower II of Earlshall; the overall average was only £6 14s 1d for the ninety-six head. Filly foals of which there were seventeen averaged £3 6s 1d and

65

nine colt foals £2 16s. Certainly there was little demand for mares and fillies during the years of the depression; at the annual sale in Perth in 1927 they were sold for only 2½ to 4½ guineas.

A few years after the start of the Earlshall stud William Mungall formed his Transy stud at Dumfermline. Starting with a pair of Shetlands in harness William Mungall became owner of some of the Londonderry females from the Seaham Harbour dispersal. His first stallion was Hector 183, by Laird of Noss 20, out of an Odin 32 mare already a winner in the show ring for William Chapman before going to Transy. Of his early stallions probably Seaweed 333 was the most influential, being the sire of Silverton, Selwood and Sonyad of Transy all three of which had powerful influence in the stud, as did Pole Star 884, brought down from Peter Manson in Shetland. Mrs William Dick took over the stud on her father's death in 1936 until most of her land was requisitioned for war purposes when, as it were, it was put into 'cold store'. No ponies were bred, some of the mares went to Harviestoun and a few at a later date to the Marshwood Stud, until such time as her stud could be started up once more. It is now being carried on successfully by Dougal Dick, the grandson of the founder.

One breeder who started her stud in the early years of the century was Mrs V. Hobart (later Lady Hobart). Not only was she extremely keen and interested in the breed but she was also a first rate judge of a pony. Some of her original stock were of Shetland origin including the stallion Captive 219 by Odin 32 which had been used very successfully by Anderson Manson. Lady Hobart later used one or two stallions of Lady Estella Hope's breeding. In addition to blacks there were a number of coloured ponies of good type and quality which had successes both in in-hand and driving classes. After her tragic death whilst hunting with the Taunton Vale, the stud was split up and sold at once and many good ponies were lost to breeders as small dealers and gypsies bought the majority

At the Seaham Harbour Sale in 1899, Francis N. M. Gourlay from Dumfriesshire bought four ponies to found his stud. One of these was a mare, Darling II 175, who figures fairly prominently in present day pedigrees six or seven generations back. This mare was the dam of Delia 2327 who bore the half brothers Drumlanrig 699, by Veracity 436, and Dunsmuir 1155, by May King of Penniwells 769;

she was also the grand dam of Dollar Boy 1242 as this pony's mother, Delilah 2708, was a daughter sired by her own halfbrother, Dvorak 375. These stallions were used a great deal and changed hands: not only did Francis Gourlay use them himself but other studs had foals sired by one or more. So this line figures fairly prominently in a number of pedigrees.

Francis Gourlay was intensely interested in his breeding stock and bred his ponies very closely: he was most anxious to keep and fix his type for they all showed immense quality. He was an interesting and amusing conversationalist, particularly so when on the subject of Shetland ponies: he was most helpful to those who sought information or advice on ponies. By 1931 he had dispersed his stud.

In about the year 1904 Dr and Mrs Charles Douglas of Auchlochan formed a small, select stud in Lanarkshire. Most of the mares were either of Londonderry breeding or boasted a certain amount of that blood. It would appear that although ponies from this stud were appreciated in other studs and some did very well in the show ring, none seem to have had a predominate influence (although Crown Prince 342 does appear frequently in pedigrees as does, to a lesser extent, his son Phoebus of Auchlochan 777). Mrs Douglas carried on the stud for a few years after her husband's death before selling out the remaining stock.

Graham Clark of Aberdeen owned many ponies but he was not a dedicated breeder. It would be hard to find any pony of his breeding to which the present day breeders are particularly indebted. However, many ponies went through his hands and he was a good judge who appreciated fit, well turned out animals.

In about 1910 Mrs Etta Duffus started her Penniwells stud in Hertfordshire. For the first year or two a stallion belonging to a neighbouring breeder was used for her mares. Mrs Duffus, having built up a useful small stud, began showing her ponies after the Great War and by 1922 was doing well at all the big shows. Her groom or stud manager was a real artist at bringing out ponies, capable of getting the most out of any pony fit to take into the ring and he most certainly gained the credit for the many successes. Beautifully schooled, polished and exact, moving smartly and truly, their ponies were eye-catching and excellent advertisements for the breed.

Without doubt Dibblitz of Penniwells 1087, a 39″ black, was the most famous pony to be brought out by the Penniwells stud. He was a good pony, a superb mover, but that he was the best ever, as has been said, is to put him too high. Sadly he left nothing of any prominence in the Stud Book and was exported to Australia in 1932 where regretfully he has left little mark. Mrs Duffus had a particularly lovely 39″ black mare, Peace of Colne, bred by Lady Hicks-Beach. She did well in the ring but again left nothing of note and she actually went to Mrs Atkinson when Mrs Duffus sold her ponies. Kitmagur of Penniwells 1246 seems to be the only son of Dibblitz who was used fairly extensively.

Regretfully, however, one must surmise that although the Duffus ponies won numerous high awards, only in one or two cases was the breeding of sufficiently good quality to expect the progeny to be of similar conformation.

At about the same time another stud, which is still in existence, was formed by Mrs W. T. R. Houldsworth of Kirkbride in Ayrshire with the brown 39″ Scrabster of Auchlochan at its head. Mrs Houldsworth did not show extensively but her son, Colonel Sir Reginald Houldsworth, a past president of the Shetland Pony Stud Book Society, does some showing and judges around the country.

A year or two later the well-known cattle, hackney pony and Clydesdale breeder, J. Ernest Kerr of Harviestoun, became a keen breeder of Shetland ponies. His foundation stock came primarily from Transy and Earlshall and for stallions, apart from those of his own breeding, he went to Francis Gourlay for Drumlanrig 699, Dollar Boy 1242 and Dunsmuir 1155. The Harviestoun ponies soon became famous as the stud piled up awards at shows in Scotland and at the R.A.S.E. Today many pedigrees show Harviestoun fairly frequently. It seems probable that the fashion for the larger pony – that is the 39″ or 40″ one – originated here. Some of these bred were fully 41″ and there is always the danger with this breed that distinct breed type may become less pronounced with the increase in size. The stallion Balgair 1403 was exported to Australia because J. E. Kerr, although admitting his quality, decided he was too small even when the stick said $38\frac{1}{2}$″. J. E. Kerr was a first class judge but he did not favour coloured ponies and he firmly believed that few, if any, good

Shetlands were to be found north of Aberdeenshire or south of the border! On his death his granddaughter took over the stud, but now only a very small number are kept.

As already stated it was immediately after the Great War when shows were resumed, that the Penniwells and Harviestoun studs came to the front to compete with Earlshall, Transy, Lady Estella Hope and other less known established breeders. Meanwhile new studs were gradually coming into being and within a few years were competing at shows. In 1922 Mrs Maurice Cox founded her Marshwood stud in Dorset with Earlshall, Maryfield and Standen blood and by 1939 had built her stock up to about fifty. However she was obliged to reduce at the beginning of the war due to agricultural regulations, and in 1945 only seven ponies remained. Since then the stud has been rebuilt mainly on the original blood. A few years later Miss A. R. Ritchie formed her Netherley stud in Kincardineshire mostly from Earlshall and Auchlochan stock; she turned to Harviestoun for stallions and has been very successful in the show ring. At about the same time Miss Enid Glasier first registered her ponies in the Stud Book. Her Avening stud in Gloucestershire has shrunk in size but she still has only chestnuts and creams. The Avening prefix is to be found in the pedigrees of many chestnut ponies. Two other studs which were formed in the twenties but are considerably smaller now than previously are those of Mrs Shearer, Newton in Monmouthshire, and Mrs Ducker whose Littlestoke stud bred light grey (sometimes called white) ponies.

A little later Mrs Atkinson started her Felbridge stud with some excellent stock from Mrs Duffus and Mrs Brian Bibby. Later Mrs Atkinson concentrated on chestnuts and greys; for the former colour the already mentioned Emmillius of Earlshall 1121 was a most successful sire and from him, amongst others, she bred two sons, Rushlight 1433 and Rearlight of Felbridge 1432. One or two Felbridge ponies were exported to Australia and have bred there successfully.

Immediately prior to the outbreak of war in 1939, the Woodbury stud was started by Miss S. Christopherson (now Mrs Harold Swannack) with mares from South Park. This stud has since left Reigate for North Devon with selected, mostly coloured mares.

There are now many studs which are making valuable contributions to the breed, but readers will appreciate the difficulty of collecting the necessary data and arriving at a date or time which is fair. Therefore the year 1939 has been taken as a suitable division for there was then a definite break in registrations and little breeding during that and the five succeeding years. Therefore the only studs included are those existing prior to the war which have continued without a break, or those which made a major contribution or had a very definite influence during the first twenty years of the Society.

Regretfully omitted also are the names of crofters and farmers in the Shetland Isles many of whom have been breeding ponies for generations. Some have kept the same strains or families for far longer than many registered in the Stud Book when it started in 1890. The task of noting down these men and something about the various ponies they bred would be an interesting but monumental task. The author tenders his sincere apologies for omissions.

Boadicea 998

# 6

# *Management*

During recent years there has been a profusion of written advice and instruction about the management of ponies and horses. Although the best management is similar for all native ponies, perhaps some observations on the special care and needs of the Shetland pony might be of help.

Because of the small size and general hardiness of this breed it can usually be kept more cheaply than other breeds.

The life and care of the pony in Shetland has already been described. Vast numbers of this breed, however, have never been within hundreds or thousands of miles of their native islands and it is with these that this chapter is concerned. Once the pony is acclimatised to other surroundings it appears to settle with equanimity to greatly varying conditions and climates.

It has often been stated and often denied that Shetland ponies, if kept and bred in a warmer climate and more luxurious conditions and grazing, will increase in size. In spite of authoritative denials this fallacy is still repeated, although hundreds of cases can be quoted to disprove it. Pure Shetland ponies, wherever they are kept and bred, will not increase in size. If, of course, ponies near the 42″ limit are mated, it is possible that some of the mature offspring will exceed the recognised limit, but this could happen anywhere. If, on the other hand, these ponies are bred in isolation and no fresh blood is introduced, the height will probably decrease in time no matter how warm and equable the climate or how rich the keep.

In the United Kingdom overhead shelter is not necessary unless there is no natural shelter where the pony can retreat from a scorching summer sun, and where there are trees, high hedges, walls or buildings to break the strong sunlight or afforded protection, nothing artificial is required. Nor is a roof needed to keep off rain or snow provided that there is some natural shelter which breaks the full force of the storms. It is remarkable where these little ponies can find refuge from the worst weather conditions, provided, of course, that they are not confined to some wretched, wire-fenced paddock. When one has seen these ponies in their native islands in severe winter storms, which may last for seven to ten days, it is easier to comprehend the comparative nonchalance with which they treat the weather in milder climates. Those who have erected shelters or sheds in fields to protect their ponies from the worst weather are often astonished by how little they are used, often only as an escape from sun and flies. It is undoubtedly useful if ponies have to be given hay, or other food, to have somewhere dry for the fodder and for this reason, if no other, shelters are useful. However, one essential for Shetland ponies, no matter where they are kept, is that there is always ample clean water available for drinking.

The Shetland pony's true habitat is not an enclosure of rich, lush pasture or a dirty little neglected paddock on which it is sometimes confined, but a rough, hard hill where it can freely roam around and pick the grazing it prefers within a large area. It is not possible for all owners to keep their stock under natural or near natural conditions but extremes must be avoided; happily most owners do, although there are ponies which unfortunately have to exist under adversity.

Shetlands kept on rich, heavily fertilized grass, either temporarily or permanently, cannot thrive in the way nature intended. Young stock, so kept, mature too quickly and become gross and coarse, whilst adult ponies become obese and prone to laminitis or founder; further there is the grave possibility of mares becoming too gross to breed and, if in-foal, danger in foaling because of excessive fat. These ponies tend to get greasy coats and may develop a propensity to rub. The healthy Shetland has a tendency to put on weight extremely easily and owners are advised to watch this carefully. Nothing is more out of keeping or ugly than a really fat pony.

If, on the other hand, the area of land available to keep a pony or ponies is strictly limited and of doubtful quality, the greatest care must be taken to render it suitable. Dirty, neglected paddocks whether large or small are never suitable, but small ones are the worst. It is unfortunately true that many ponies of all breeds are kept in highly unsuitable, dirty enclosures. If a pony has to be kept in a small field or paddock it should be kept very clean and the grass should be well looked after. All horses and ponies are difficult grazers and will neglect grass which appears to be highly edible, grazing at grass so short that they are almost eating the earth in which it grows: consequently pastures on which horses or ponies are grazing require considerable attention, particularly if the area is small. If the fields are sufficiently large it is beneficial, and advisable to introduce grazing cattle in addition to, or instead of, ponies if the field can be spared for a period. Sheep are not of the same value to the pasture since they graze short grass like the ponies, but cattle will pull out coarse and other rank long grass which ponies will not touch, however hungry. Should the enclosures be really small, or the number of ponies too great, the practice of removing the droppings, preferably every day, is to be recommended. It must be remembered that horses and ponies, whether in stables or out at grass, are very clean feeders and dirt and staleness of food will almost certainly put them off their feed.

A pony, like other animals, may pick up some poisonous plant: this is a serious mishap but probably the Shetland has a fairly sound sense for not eating harmful plants or substances. Various fatalities have been reported from time to time but these are probably more likely to occur in early spring when plants are freshly growing and the pony is tempted to eat young green sprouts or plants which have sprung up before or with the first shoots of grass. Some plants are apparently far more poisonous to ruminants than to horses or ponies. Bracken is a cumulative poison but it is doubtful if ponies would ever eat a sufficient quantity, if any at all, to harm them. If they were kept on an enclosure – no matter how large – where there was nothing else to eat, then this would be a case of severe ill treatment and malnutrition. One writer of a letter a few years back stated that Shetland ponies ate much bracken in their native isles without harm: he had failed to ascertain, however, that there is no bracken growing in the Shetland Islands!

The manurial or fertilising problem of the enclosures on which ponies are grazed should be considered and the owner who has slight knowledge of agriculture should consult either a farmer or agricultural adviser about suitable procedure. If, however, neither of these have had experience of the grazing or keep of ponies or horses, any suggestion to use nitrogenous fertilizer in any quantity should be questioned.

If kept on large enclosures of rough or hill land the Shetland will not normally require supplementary feeding during winter except, perhaps, during long spells of snow or hard frosts. If, however, they are in normal sized fields where there is insufficient grass throughout winter to keep them in good order, a small quantity of hay or oat straw may be required to prevent a great loss of condition. Ponies kept in small paddocks do require some feeding during the cold, wet, hard period of the year. They should get a regular supply of sound hay given in a rack or in nets: these nets should be securely tied up and be sufficiently high to ensure that a pony will not get a foot caught. This advice about winter feeding is for adult stock: developing fillies and colts may require a little more, or a longer feeding period. A small feed each day of bruised oats, barley or proprietory nuts, but definitely only a small quantity – probably $1\frac{1}{2}$ lbs. per day – is as much as any filly should require.

Foals do need extra feed when weaned and during their first winter but it is difficult to lay down any given quantity. The owner must decide the amount according to the condition of the young stock, taking into account also the weather and the state and size of the field they are in; in fact strict observation is most necessary if the ponies are to be kept in the best condition, neither too fat nor too lean. It is preferable to divide the food into halves and to feed one half in the morning and the other in the afternoon, always at the same time each day. Not only do ponies do better when given small feeds regularly, but another advantage of putting out two feeds a day is that the foals will be looked over twice a day. The afternoon feed should be given in time for the foals to finish it before dark. Hay will be required but only as much as they will clear up, and here again it is safer and less wasteful to give it in racks or haynets.

Ponies are clean feeders. Care must be taken to see that any receptacle used for feeding them is kept clean and dry. If any feed is ever left in any receptacle the reason should be ascertained: it may be that too much was given, that the feed or mixture was unpalatable or that the tin or manger was dirty. Of course if a pony is ill this is a different matter, but with normal healthy stock one of the above three reasons is probably the cause and none of them should really happen under the best management and observation. Buckets or other containers for drinking water must also be kept clean and filled.

Owners have their own preference for different feeding mixtures; they may possibly have found certain ingredients to be suitable. Nowadays the procuring of some feeding stuffs is difficult; some are so expensive and some of such indifferent quality that it is almost impossible to make mixture suggestions that will meet every case. At one time the most common feed was bruised oats and broad bran with possibly a very small addition of boiled linseed, or just linseed oil. Bruised barley can be substituted for oats; others feed calf or even cattle mixtures which are not only expensive but usually unnecessarily

Circus ponies feeding

high in protein. Taking everything into account it is probably advisable today to feed suitable nuts, made by various manufacturers especially for different ages and types of horse and pony. These are a safe feed made from first class quality ingredients and provided the manufacturers' instructions on quantity and so on are regarded, ponies will do well on them. Where the owner grows his or her own grain it might be best to feed this in one way or another, but again the question arises of what to mix with it. At one time one could get broad bran without difficulty. Now owing apparently to different methods of milling wheat and different uses to which the residues are put, the old fashioned, beautiful, floury broad bran seems a thing of the past. It is very scarce.

The feeding of ponies when they are in stables being prepared for shows is dealt with in another chapter. If they happen to be in stables for purposes other than this, perhaps due to illness, a special diet may be required. If incarcerated from injury or accident great care must be taken not to overfeed or give too much heating feed, in fact very little 'hard' feed should be given. In these cases give just a small quantity of suitable nuts or, better still, a feed composed largely of broad bran (if procurable) with a sprinkling of molasses or black treacle dissolved in a tiny quantity of hot water – just sufficient to barely damp the feed.

Incidentally, it should have been mentioned before that damping all feeds is advisable, except nuts. Damping does not mean a wet feed; on the contrary just sufficient water or treacle and water is sprinkled lightly on the top of the feed and then thoroughly mixed by hand.

There are various feed supplements, spices and so on which some owners may prefer to use. A number of manufacturers advertise these, but provided the pony is in good health and the feed palatable and clean, it is unlikely that a Shetland pony will refuse. Seaweed meal is a supplement which they appreciate: a maximum of 5% of their feed is sufficient, but it is now very expensive. Rock salt is another supplementary they enjoy and a lump placed out in the field in which they graze is an essential unless one of the manufactured blocks of salt and mineral is supplied.

The owner must use his discretion as to quantity but it is advisable to err on the short side rather than give too much. As a guide it is found that *up to* 2 lbs per head per day is ample for weaned foals during their first winter only and this maximum amount, unless the weather is very hard and cold, need not be given until January or February. In spring the foals will let the owner know that the feed may be reduced, for as soon as they taste a little fresh growth there is a tendency not to clean up their feed.

It is advisable, unless there is sound veterinary reason otherwise, that mares foal in a field or paddock. It is not at all usual to place them in boxes or stables and it is better for the mare to know the enclosure rather than to be put in a strange paddock just before foaling. As a general rule foaling for Shetland mares is normal and quick, but it is advisable to keep foaling mares where they may be frequently seen and looked over. The less the mare is interfered with the better: unless there is some deviation from normal delivery it is best for the person in charge to remain at a distance. If there is reason to suspect that delivery is not going as it should, or obvious difficulties have arisen, skilled help should be summoned immediately. It is unwise to try and assist in this task without basic knowledge and great care should be taken both for the mare's physical well-being and hygienic considerations. A normal foaling should be over in about twenty minutes or less with the mare and foal soon on their feet. Once the foal is dry and has sucked there need be little anxiety for its immediate future.

It is advisable not to have barren or yeld mares running with foaling mares or fillies as a foal may possibly be stolen through jealousy. Once this has happened it is no easy task to restore confidence again to mother and foal.

A young or nervous mare may not dry her foal by licking; should this be so, it is well worth sprinkling a little salt on the foal's back before having to resort to hand drying. The mare, once she tastes the salt, will as a rule continue the job she should have done without such encouragement.

There is little danger in allowing a stallion, especially an experienced entire to be with foaling mares. It is most unusual for them to interfere in any way and they will normally allow the foaling mare without question to go off into a corner or secluded part of the field away from the others.

One sometimes sees it written that pony mares, when foaled, should be placed on good or rich grass: this is doubtful advice as so much depends on what sort of pasture they had previously, the size of the enclosure, and so on. The Shetland pony mare has quite phenomenal ability to produce milk, as have all Shetland mammals. If some breeders of Shetland ponies, strangers to the islands, saw some of the grazings on which mares rear their foals successfully year after year, they might revise their definition of good grass necessary to produce adequate milk for raising foals. Certainly it is better that the mare should be on reasonably good pasture which is clean, but to put nursing mares on seeds or other heavily fertilized land is a grave mistake. The mares will get far too fat as well as produce milk. If one considers animals in the wild it is natural for them to put on sufficient flesh during the summer to be in good condition by winter; then to gradually lose their condition or flesh so that in the spring and at foaling or calving time they are almost lean and in correct condition for giving birth. Under domestic conditions, however, if in the autumn animals are fat, they have a tendency not to lose much flesh in winter as we see that they are on reasonably good keep, and often fodder or feed is given when it is not really required.

If a mare produced a surplus of milk for her foal there is the possibility that it may cause the foal to scour; this should not be mistaken for scour a foal may develop when its dam is in season and which will quickly clear up. If a foal's scour persists, an old effective cure is to put mother and foal on a pasture which has recently been dressed with lime, if such an enclosure is available. Veterinary science has produced various drugs which can be given, but if a cure can be made without recourse to these so much the better.

The method of weaning foals is controversial but if one considers every aspect, the one which causes the least shock or suffering to both mare and foal is that which severs all relationship – sight, smell and hearing – at once. This is the method which is most usually practised and must be the least distressful in the end, though some mares show little regret when big, strong foals are removed from them, nor is great distress shown by well grown, five or six month old offspring.

Having decided that the foal or foals should be weaned, it is recommended that the mares with their foals are led into a box or yard and, when the foals are identified, the mares should be taken away, leaving their foals in the box. The mares should then be removed at once to a bare or barish field as far away as possible, so that any calling from box or field is not heard by either party. They should not be able to see each other at the time or later, if the foals are turned into a field, for at least a month. Unless a mare is really desperately uncomfortable the vessel should never be touched, as any drawing off of milk will only encourage its secretion. A really large dose of Epsom Salts (up to six tablespoonfuls) repeated if necessary, will assist in stopping secretion. It is good if the mares can be put in a large field where they can take exercise, as a mare who shows distress at the loss of her foal may well gallop or trot around the field calling and fretting, which process will in itself help to take the milk off her.

The foals may fret for twenty-four hours but soon settle down and feed. It is quite a sound idea for a few days before weaning, if no feeding has ever been already given, to give the mare a small, light feed – just a few oats mixed with chopped hay. This will enable the foal to learn to feed from a bucket or trough so that when weaned there will be no difficulty in getting it to put its nose in a trough.

It is very rare for a Shetland foal to refuse to eat at weaning: it may take a day or two to start on hard food if it has not had any with its dam, but it will seldom refuse hay. If such an eventuality does occur a little fresh grass scattered amongst and on top of a small feed may well start the shy feeder.

If foals have not already been handled, or have been handled very little, weaning time is an excellent opportunity to continue their education, getting them used to a head collar and to being led as well as becoming accustomed to having their legs and feet stroked. However, do let them settle for forty-eight hours before starting training.

It is hardly necessary to emphasise that identification must be infallible. If there are a number of very similar foals, all blacks in particular, careful notes of marks or peculiarities should be made. If the numbers are large a system of hoof branding is to be recommended though this method of marking has the big drawback of having to be undertaken approximately every three or four months.

The most certain method is that of lip tattooing although this, also, can prove to be not entirely reliable. Some black ponies have patches of dark pigmentation on the inside of the lower lip where the tattoo marks have to be placed: therefore the greatest care should be taken to see that the ink or dye is absolutely effective. It is interesting to note, in respect of identification, that some countries insist on body branding and others on the lip tattooing of all ponies registered in their Stud Books.

In this country the Shetland Pony Stud Book Society has always assumed that all its members are upright and honest and that none of them would ever be responsible for mistaken identity of ponies, either purposely or inadvertently.

In any discussion on the breeding of ponies the topic of serving of mares will arise and age, time and method may be argued. A two year old filly, if she is well grown and in good order, can well be put to a stallion, but if the filly may be wanted for show the following spring or summer then obviously she should not be put in foal. Before it is decided to have a filly served the owner is strongly advised to thoroughly scrutinise her. It is worthwhile calling in a more experienced friend to help make quite certain that she is good enough to breed from: that her jaws are correct, that she has not a slipping stifle nor goes excessively wide behind or is extremely cow-hocked, in fact that she has no outstanding faults which would probably be handed down to her offspring. It is just as bad, or almost as bad, to breed from a female with glaring – and probably hereditary – faults as it is from such a male. This sort of filly should be sold without pedigree as a riding pony or pet.

The commonly used method of service is for the stallion to be running out at grass and the mare or filly to be taken to the field and turned loose. The service in hand of Shetland ponies is to be deprecated: firstly it is not the natural method, secondly some stallions, especially those which have already worked in freedom, are shy in hand, and thirdly because many owners of mares are not knowledgeable enough to know just when and how much to encourage or interfere with the mating. This mating in hand is a practice which should only be done under the auspices of someone who really knows what he is doing for the best results and avoidance of trouble and even danger to the ponies. In past days the stallion leader, or man in studs or with travelling stallions, was always one who had been thoroughly taught his job and had learnt many wrinkles of behaviour and so on during the seasons.

Shetland stallions are as a rule civil and understanding when out at grass with mares and one seldom comes across one that is hard or difficult with the average mare. Average is purposely used here because there are undoubtedly some mares which are difficult and stallions have been known to become exasperated and possibly bitten them up or driven them away. It has happened that mares have been driven away so hard that they have jumped fences to be free of persecution; but these are very much the exceptions and it may be found that these mares will not breed.

There was a case a few years ago in Shetland when a Premium stallion refused to have any crossbred or larger mares on the grazing and was responsible for driving away a 15.2 h.h. cross Clydesdale mare.

One trouble which can occur with Shetlands, as it can in other breeds, is a condition when mares appear to be more or less perpetually in season and when running with a stallion continually worry him, especially when another mare comes on heat. This is due, as a rule, to cystic ovary and should be treated immediately by a veterinary surgeon: there are treatments involving hormones which normally will allay this trouble. Urgent treatment is necessary and the mare should be removed from the field where the stallion is running as the owner may find that a number of mares are failing to be settled due to the behaviour of this affected mare.

Fillies, also, can be very jealous and require careful watching particularly if they are running with a young or fairly inexperienced stallion for they may prevent others being served.

The feet of Shetlands are usually hard and tough although they vary in different strains of pony. Some chestnuts have much softer feet than others, but probably the white feet of a skewbald or a piebald are the softest and most quickly worn. As a rule this breed have little trouble with their feet. I have come across aged ponies which have never even had to have a rasp near their hoofs, but normally it is quite impossible to say how frequently this happens as

the rate of growth of hoof varies from one pony to the next and naturally much depends on the ground on which they are running. If ponies
are running on soft, peaty or mossy ground it is probable that trimming
will be necessary more frequently than for ponies which are kept on
rocky or even gravel soils, as here the abrasive action of the ground
wears down new growth. If ponies are running on land where there is
grit or fine gravel, and particularly where these substances may be
mixed with mud (as in a gateway or round a water trough or crossing
of ditches) grit may be picked up which forces its way between the
sole and the wall of the hoof. This can lead to lameness, but it very
often causes a misshapen foot as the wall will grow out to relieve
pressure on the sensitive laminae. A blacksmith should be called in
to pare away the crack with his searcher knife and the gravel or small
stone should be carefully removed, making sure that no foreign matter
remains. If the cavity is fairly big a small wad of tow saturated with
Stockholm or Archangel tar should be pressed in; if, however, the
cavity is small it may be advisable to leave it open.

'Sweet itch' is a tiresome and horrible complaint for a pony as it
causes an almost constant irritation of the parts affected. It is tiresome and frustrating for the owner also, as no cure has yet been
found that is thoroughly effective in all cases, nor is much known
about the complaint. Various theories are propounded but none seem
to be positive. It does appear that there is a definite hereditary
tendency for ponies in certain lines to contract this affliction but it
does not appear contagious; further there might well be some slight
variations of it. It has been found that a foal brought down from
Shetland to richer ground and a milder climate may, as a yearling
and/or as a two year old, develop a condition similar to 'sweet itch',
but at three years old or maturity the condition does not appear nor
does it do so subsequently. Yet there are ponies, mares in particular,
which year in, year out suffer the same distressing affliction. Other
unexplained cases have occurred when the foals of a stallion develop
this trouble as fillies, yet the stallion has never been affected nor have
his forebears ever been suspected of having it.

The symptoms of the complaint are as follows: the affected pony
suffers from what must be an intense irritation, of, usually, the
mane, particularly the lower part around the withers, the tail and

tail-head; the skin becomes corrugated, hard and swollen and the pony wants to rub all the time; consequently the skin is often broken and the hair broken and rubbed off. Various injections and lotions have been tried and although some of the latter, in particular, may have a temporary palliative effect, no real cure has yet been discovered.

In Queensland, Australia, a similar complaint exists but this is caused by a 'bug' and it is apparently possible, though difficult, to control it.

Of course ponies will rub even when they have not got 'sweet itch' and it often seems that the filly which had such lovely hair and was to have been shown has rubbed off half her mane and broken most of the hair in her tail! This rubbing in summer is usually due to high condition and a convenient wire fence (preferably with a barbed strand!)

If young ponies are not in tiptop condition at about the beginning of the New Year, it may be that lice are the cause. At the slightest sign of rubbing or scratching in winter it is advisable to apply a known brand of louse powder. Do this on a day when the ponies' coats are dry and make certain that the powder gets down through the hair into the skin; this can be quite a task with a Shetland in winter coat, but it is well worth the effort.

For bruises, bumps or strains the old-fashioned remedy is most effective – the application of copious cold water, preferably through a hosepipe, and complete rest. Damage to an eye is not a common complaint but it does sometimes happen and as the eye is such an important organ any damage must be treated with great care. The Shetland should have a prominent eye and it sometimes happens that it is kicked or scratched or pricked by a thorn, or it may get some foreign substance in it. Expert advice should be sought in all these cases. Sometimes, however, one finds a slight inflammation in the eye of a foal or young pony or perhaps an adult. If on examination there is no sign at all of damage – and this must be very definitely ascertained – then bathing the eye in cold tea will greatly assist in reducing the inflammation: possibly it may have to be done for some consecutive days. This is an old-fashioned but effective cure.

One of the most important constituents of management is the

control and prevention of worm infestation. All equines are subject to this trouble and Shetlands are no exception. In fact ponies which spend the greater part of their lives at grass are more susceptible: the smaller the enclosures and the heavier the concentration of ponies on the ground the greater the probability they will be seriously affected unless steps are taken to reduce or eliminate the risk. I shall not describe or examine the various worms and their life history which can be found in articles on the subject as well as descriptions which most manufacturers of anthelmintics put out with their products. I shall discuss, however, prevention, or at least the impeding of infestation.

If ponies are grazed in small enclosures the ideal way to keep down the possibility of worm infection is to daily lift the droppings, although this is an expensive and somewhat laborious task. If this is not possible the scattering of the droppings can help, as the eggs which may be in the droppings are deprived of the heat and shelter necessary for development. If possible do not keep any ponies on the same enclosure all the year round: move them off and substitute other animals, preferably cattle, to graze off the field. It really is a matter of trying to keep the pastures clean and thus reduce the risk of ponies picking up the eggs. If the grazing is a large field which is not heavily stocked there is less likelihood of rapid infestation, whilst where ponies are grazing on really large enclosures or on hill or moorland the risk of infestation is reduced still further.

Great care must be taken to ensure that one's ponies do not become 'wormy'. If ponies lose condition, if their coat becomes harsh and staring and they generally lack bloom, it is likely that worms are the cause. This is easily ascertained by taking a dung sample and having a count of worm eggs made. There are various anthelmintics on the market for the various worm infestations and the correct dose of these can be given in perfect safety. Sometimes the presence of worms can be detected quite clearly in the droppings, and it is a good practice to examine them now and then, breaking up the faeces carefully to expose as much as possible. If, however, no worms are seen, this must not be taken as evidence that the pony concerned is quite free of these parasites. It is the practice in some studs to administer routine doses for the control of worms: this may be necessary but it is not a practice which meets with universal approval. The regular dosing of stock should not really be necessary, nor is it desirable, because probably many animals who do not require the drug are given it, quite unnecessarily and surely not beneficially.

For thousands of years horses have been used in far greater numbers than they are even now and for very many years they have been used for fast work, racing, harness and hunting. They were fit and well able to go long distances at good speed. Yet until thirty or forty years ago the only cure for the red worm and others was the unpleasant, un-wieldy stomach pump which, after due preparation of the subject, was introduced through a nostril into the stomach and then pumped in some poisonous fluid. It was altogether a horrid process and not without danger for the health of the subject.

It was the practice to 'physic' horses or ponies when they were turned out to grass and again when they came in from grass. The 'physic' was a pretty powerful laxative. Stud grooms and others had their own recipes for the concoction of these balls, the main ingredients probably being aloes, ginger and oil of Chenopodium. Some of these balls were drastic but presumably were quite effective in keeping the worms in check. Shetland ponies have roamed the hills of Shetland for thousands of years yet it is quite certain that until, say, twenty years ago, not one had ever been 'wormed'. At times a pony, probably an old mare, in poor condition was brought in from the hill and grazed around the outfall from the byre, which also included the slurry from the earth closet: the pony would greedily graze the strong, succulent, green growth of grass which, after the hard fare of the hill, would act like a dose of salts: this, then, was normally the only physic a pony received. It is undeniable that ponies in Shetland do have worms, in fact some of the older mares may well have tapeworm, which is unusual in ponies or horses generally. But then it is recorded that even trout in Shetland have the same trouble!

It must not on any account be assumed that the control of worms in ponies is being derided or rejected. It is most essential to maintain careful observation and to take remedial steps when required, but the convenient though expensive method of regular routine dosing may be questioned.

Not only in the question of worm control but in other ways, also, the management of Shetland ponies away from the islands differs greatly. True, the conditions under which they live are very different but perhaps a great deal of the management meted out to them now is too artificial and can undermine their inbred hardiness and independence.

Under normal care and observation, which is the due of every animal from white mice upwards, the Shetland pony will thrive and prosper.

There has been much written in recent years about the care of horses and ponies and I do not intend to reiterate all the advice given by various authorities. However, it might be advisable just to mention one or two of the more common ailments or infections that do affect all ponies and horses.

Such is the bot, the maggot form of the gadfly, which during the summer months lays its yellow eggs on the hair, usually on the legs. Years ago a young man whose knowledge of horses was not as profound as he would have one believe, was walking amongst some ponies. He drew attention to the yellow eggs on the legs of some and a gadfly hovering around awaiting the opportunity to lay more eggs, and lisped,

'It's stwange how the bees can get pollen off the ponies' legs!!'

To detach the eggs a cloth impregnated with toilet paraffin wiped down the legs over the eggs effectively dissolves the adhesive by which they adhere until normally licked off by the pony. A singeing lamp may be used for this purpose but lamp paraffin is not recommended as it sometimes blisters the skin. If swallowed by the host these eggs eventually hatch and remain as maggots in the stomach where they can cause serious disorders. If dosing for worms fails to rectify a pony's condition there is a possibility that the cause may be bots and a dung sample in spring should be analysed to detect the presence or absence of the bot.

Laminitis is a condition to which some Shetlands are subject outside their native islands, and is normally due to their becoming gross and overfat on rich pasture. This condition, at times called 'founder', is an intense inflammation of the laminae of the feet causing them to come apart and the pedal bone to press down the sole of the foot. It is most painful for the animal afflicted and veterinary advice should be sought at once. If treatment is given in time there are drugs which can be effective. Standing the pony in wet mud and frequent applications of cold water will help reduce the heat and pain, large doses of Epsom Salt will help to cool the blood and ample fresh water should be available. This condition may lead to deformity of the feet. In-foal or nursing mares are not subject to this: it affects barren mares and geldings which have become gross – usually those that are running on rich pasture or heavily fertilized temporary pasture. It seems that certain bloodlines are more susceptible than others, but it is difficult to even guess why this is so. It is possible that particular areas of the country may be more likely to induce the condition. In Australia the incidence has caused some consternation as it has appeared fairly frequently amongst ponies which are run on not first class pasture; it suggests the possibility that it is induced by sudden growth of grass due to moisture on warm ground.

It is of course important to look out for symptoms of illness or disorder at any time, particularly during and at the conclusion of travel. This is especially important with ponies, especially those which may not have been handled a great deal.

Shock or travel tetany sometimes develops in which the pony shows signs of distress. The breathing becomes rapid and sometimes laboured, sweating is profuse, the temperature may rise slightly, the jaws are affected by muscular contraction, the pony may stagger and the legs become stiff. Immediate stabling in a darkened, quiet box with plenty of cold water for drinking is the first essential and a request should be made to the vet to administer an intravenous injection of calcium gluconate solution. Complete rest and a light diet are required for a few days: if the jaw contraction is such that the pony is unable to eat normally, milk and raw eggs may have to be given.

Pneumonia can develop suddenly. Usually the first symptoms are rapid and somewhat laboured breathing which is shown by the movement of the flanks and abdomen with dilating nostrils. The temperature will be high. Immediate treatment is called for and modern drugs, promptly administered by the veterinary surgeon, do normally aid a fairly quick recovery, but nursing is important and the sick pony should be in a quiet, airy box with plenty of good dust-free bedding.

There are numerous other disorders or infections which may or may not be met with over a period of years, but the ones most likely to crop up are probably those already mentioned.

One thing that is sometimes lost sight of is the importance of good nursing. No matter what drugs and medicines a pony may be given it is supremely important that it has confidence in its attendant and fully understands that it can expect quiet, warmth and fresh air. Often in cases of illness and injury the appetite has to be coaxed back and here the attendant must spend a long time, if necessary, trying to find the 'something' that will entice the patient to pick a little food and subsequently regain its appetite. A few blades of green grass, which can usually be found in some sheltered corner at any time of year, if scattered on a small feed may be just what is needed to start the pony eating again: this is the sort of thing that matters. The patient must have quiet – no bustling in with cheery greeting to the box – but a very quiet approach; if the patient does take notice of you then a quiet word is sufficient and a quick look round to see all is in order. Possibly the bedding needs a shake up but this must be done very quietly, without fuss, and any administration of medicine or applications should be done in the same quiet way.

An old boat on Bressay converted into a stable

# 7

# *Uses*

The past uses of Shetland ponies in their native islands, and their significant economic value to crofters have been described in an earlier chapter.

Now the purpose of their existence in the islands has completely changed for they are no longer used on the croft since mechanical power has taken their place. However, the affection that is felt for the ponies and the fact that in terms of cash they are a good investment showing a fair return, have ensured that they are still kept and bred there. They are not much used in Shetland at the present time but of those young ponies which leave the islands every year many go to buyers for children's mounts and so on.

Obviously if many ponies are bred, whether in the Shetland Isles or in Scotland, England or Wales, there must be a use for them. It would be ridiculous if all breeders went on producing Shetland ponies merely to sell to each other to breed: such a situation would be disastrous to any breed. It is in circumstances like this that the calamitous reproduction of animals is perpetuated, producing types with astonishing, extraneous, exaggerated points which are merely fashionable for show purposes. It is horrifying to think that this could ever happen to the Shetland breed but it should be borne in mind. These sort of changes may come gradually and the impact on the breed is at first almost unnoticeable though it may, like some insidious disease, affect so many ponies that suddenly it is realised that the breed has been done untold harm.

Jumping

So it is the duty of every breeder or those interested in the Shetland pony to encourage its use in every way. It would be hard to find a more willing, courageous yet docile branch of the equine race, one that if properly handled will give years of faithful and economic service.

Some ponies are kept just for ornamental purposes, a role which they fulfil extremely well. Running in a park or in large fields around a country house they provide continual interest and can well add to the picturesque surroundings. Provided some care and interest is given them there is little danger to the breed and it may well encourage others who see them to invest in a few ponies for themselves. It has happened, however, that such a herd of ponies has deteriorated badly through the use of inferior stallions. The owner has decided that skewbalds, for instance, would be impressive and without much thought has brought in some indifferent entire which sires skewbald foals but which may be of extremely poor conformation. Therefore, though the colour is desirable, the young stock are merely coloured rubbish.

Certainly not all ponies kept for ornament or as a hobby are in-differently bred. Many owners take care and trouble and do their best to find suitable stallions for service of their stock. Some of the ponies kept like this are the pensioners which carried their owners a few years earlier. They have been kept on possibly in the hope that they will provide a mount for some child not yet born.

Some owners with a very developed commercial sense fail to place any sentimental value on their animals. They consider it is foolish, which is nonsense, but it is equally nonsensical to carry sentimentality too far and can lead to great harm to the animal concerned and cause the owner much trouble and sorrow. One must always remember that a pony has not got the objective reasoning power of the human; its immediate needs are comfort, food, water and shelter. Unquestionably, however, Shetland ponies have tremendous character, marvellous memories and show more sense and intelligence than other breeds.

To observe a scarcely handled Shetland pony being loaded into an open boat and taken across open water with hardly a movement, which, if made, might cause serious difficulties not only to its companions but to the boatmen and the boat itself, is an edifying sight. It shows, as much as anything, that it realises the danger and that although it would not allow man to approach too close when on land, it will trust him if in some quite unknown, possibly hazardous situation.

Shetlands can be trained easily and quickly for various purposes. It is only necessary to gain the complete confidence of the pony before attempting anything else: this can be done with ninety-nine ponies out of 100 quite quickly if the handler will only show patience and move quietly so he never becomes startled or gets a fright.

Apart from keeping these ponies for ornamental purposes or for breeding to show, they have many other uses. Their main use now is as children's first mounts: many of these are used for driving as well which must come second in a list of the uses for which they are kept and bred. A considerable number still remain with the owners who have outgrown them: sometimes they run as pets with larger ponies or horses, now just companionable pensioners. Then a number are kept and trained for circus work, probably more than actually perform.

A few are probably still used for light work on a farm or in a garden but their use for odd carting jobs is hardly economic unless the owner or one of the family do the work in their spare time or it is light occupation for a retired person. Virtually none are now used for peat flitting or such jobs in Shetland. In the late autumn of 1973, after an unprecedently wet summer in Shetland, an elderly crofter's wife bemoaned the fact that they had not got their peats home during the summer as the ground had been too wet for their tractor to get near the bank. However, if they had still had the ponies it would not have been a case of having to buy expensive coal to keep their range going all winter.

At one time the flitting of peats by pony must have been common, yet probably many Shetlanders have never seen it being done nor even know how it was done. The ponies used were mares, some with foals at foot: some of these mares were only handled at the time of the peat flitting and for the greater part of the year would be running on the hills. Once they had been used for this task and had been brought in and prepared they went about it without further bother; some did not even have halters put on. Usually the peats would be flitted whilst the children were not at school: some of the boys helped which meant they were working from morn till night and trudging back and forth from the peat bank to the croft on a long summer day could be fairly exhausting. The ponies themselves needed little real attention as they fell into routine once they had made the journey to and fro, and continued until 'de afbendin gang' or the last trip of the day was over.

The equipment for this task of peat flitting probably changed little over a long period and was virtually all made on the croft with materials to hand. Firstly a pad of coarse woollen material was placed on the pony's back, though in latter years a folded sack was more usual. Over this was laid a mat woven of Shetland oat straw which was more pliable and tougher than ordinary oat straw: this was the 'flackie'. Then the 'klibber' was placed on. This was a simple type of pack saddle made from two flat wooden boards from which were projecting handles or horns pivoting on a wooden pin, the 'varnagl', to allow the boards to fit more comfortably along the pony's back according to the width of its barrel. The tops of these horns or handles were fashioned into inverted hooks. From the lower edge of the klibber

Flitting peats in Shetland

board ('deklibberbrod') were rope loops ('quinteks') to which the girth ('warnegrit') was fastened. This was usually of light rope bound with cloth so that it did not cut or chafe the pony. In addition a crupper ('tailgirt'), also made of padded rope, was attached round the horns of the klibber.

If the load was to be peat, potatoes or articles unlike hay, flexible baskets made of rushes or floss called 'rivakeshies' were used to hold the goods. These had a loop at the bottom as well as two at the top so that when emptying it was easily and quickly done by holding the bottom loop and spilling out the contents. Before these 'keshies' were put on the 'maishies' were first hooked on: these were large nets made of cord from rushes. The nearside maishie was hooked over the offside horn of the klibber and vice versa, then the keshies were hooked on, and finally the maishie was picked up and pieces of peat large enough not to slip through the mesh were placed in it before it was secured to the horn of the klibber with the 'fettle', a loop of cord

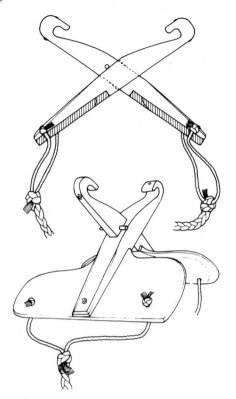

Diagram of klibber

attached to the maishie. It was the usual custom to have two lots of keshies in use so that one set was being filled whilst the other set was in transit. Another use for the klibber is mentioned by Hibbert. When in Shetland in 1822 he saw it being used as a side saddle: presumably the horns would act as pommels.

There is no doubt that a good, well made Shetland pony has no rival as a child's first mount. Some people deny this but none of their reasons will hold water, for the examples they quote of horrors or difficulties are all based on exceptions and not on the general run of properly trained and handled ponies. Anyone can find easily tales of dreadful ponies and horses of all breeds: nearly all of them have as their cause the mishandling or mismanagement of the animal. If one hears a tale of woe in which a small pony is involved that pony is certain to be called a Shetland even though it may be only remotely connected. It may be true that the Shetland pony does not cross well with other breeds since, apart from other reasons, the Shetland has slight differences in bone structure from that of other horses and ponies.

Sometimes it is said that Shetlands are too wide for children to straddle and it could do them harm. This is nonsense, for a suitable Shetland pony, in good order, is no wider and in most cases not so wide as other, larger breeds. Of course if people put small children on very fat or in foal ponies it might be true, but this should never happen. Unfortunately there is much ignorant, stupid talk and action about suitable ponies for children.

Often some thick necked, straight shouldered, docile pony has a bridle pushed into its mouth, a saddle placed on its back and a child placed on it. It is then termed a quiet child's mount. So it may be, but how can it be properly controlled or how can the child learn the first rudiments of riding when the pony has no 'mouth' at all, no manners and not the faintest idea of what is expected of it?

The Shetland of true type, however, which was bred as a general purpose pony for countless generations, makes a really splendid pony for a child. Through it a child can gain confidence, understanding and elementary horse mastership. For this is the time for any child to acquire a basic knowledge of ponies, (possibly quite unconsciously), through intimate association with an animal which has confidence in her and she in it. Seldom does it happen that children and ponies who are companions and spend much time together ever have a real mishap. The mishaps happen to children who have not had the good fortune to be brought up with a pony, to trust their mount and treat it with confidence and kindness.

When one starts to train a pony for children's use it is important to gain its complete confidence. Then, no matter what happens around it or what is, within bounds, done to it, it has a nonchalant attitude and ignores disturbances which might well send more highly strung animals into a panic. It is remarkable how quickly the average Shetland will soon be 'bombproof' if treated in the right way and it is important that it should be so trained if it is to be the mount of a small child, particularly one who may be nervous. It must allow anyone to handle it all over; it must allow its feet to be picked up without hesitation; it must not mind its tail being pulled round or the handling of its head or neck; it must not flinch or start at sudden movements or if a rope or stick is waved in close vicinity. It is most important that the pony should be absolutely quiet and confident. During this time of confidence gaining, the pony is taught to lead on either rein, to halt and to walk on until it is obedient to voice alone and does not need to be stopped by pressure on the noseband or a touch with stick or hand. It must turn easily and not be pushed or dragged around.

Then arises this question: is it to be lunged or is it to be long reined? This is a question on which opinion is divided but whichever technique is used must be done properly. Unless the person has been taught to lunge a pony the use of long reins may be preferable. How many ponies and horses does one see, possibly at a show, being correctly lunged? How often does one see some sorry sights? It is essential that the pony's forehand and quarters are moving in the same track, that its head is not twisted round with the pony leaning away from the rein and that it is moving freely, not stopping to snatch mouthfuls of grass whilst a frantic handler waves a short riding cane and chirrups it on. If lunging is to be efficient the pony must move round freely both at walk and at trot; it must be taught to turn whilst moving; it must learn to stop, walk, trot and come to the handler's hand by command. These movements all take time to teach and there should be no rush to finish training since spending insufficient time on the job will only turn out failures.

During these lessons the pony may have a bit in its mouth but not until the training is advanced should the bit be used. It is advisable when the bit is first put in to do so when the pony is in its box and only leave it in the mouth for fifteen or twenty minutes: the lunge rein should be buckled to the back 'D' of the leather head-collar unless a cavesson is being used. The handler should carry a light lunging whip and the glass fibre ones are lighter and easier to handle.

From the very beginning and throughout training the use of the voice is strongly advocated. It should not be unduly raised for the intention is to give confidence and friendship, not to frighten. Any command like 'Walk', 'Walk on' or 'Whoa' should be given sharply, but quiet, encouraging remarks undoubtedly do help with the training.

The frequent giving of titbits, bread, sugar or nuts is an unwise practice.

If it is decided to long rein, the first procedure is similar to that at the beginning of these lessons. Whether lunging or long reining an assistant should lead the pony until it is used to being controlled from a distance: this will not take long and normally a day or two will suffice. The pony soon realises that it is being 'led from behind' and only if it is startled by some object in front is it likely to turn around. As in lunging the pony must be taught to walk, trot and halt when commanded. In long reining it is necessary for the pony to wear a roller or surcingle to which it may become accustomed in its box, as with the bit.

The roller has a ring on each side through which the reins are run and must have a crupper to make certain it does not slip forward or twist. As in lunging the reins are not attached to the bit until the pony is well advanced in training, but should be buckled to the 'D's on each side of the headcollar. The reins may be run straight from the handler's hands to the noseband but this method of threading them is most satisfactory as the pressure is not so direct and it assists in keeping up the head. The raising of the head is, provided the pony has a reasonably good conformation, largely a matter of fitness as well as training. Also, as in lunging, the handler should carry a light lunge whip and should not walk close to the pony, but allow a reasonable length of rein between them.

Whether the pony has been long reined, lunged, or a mixture of both (which is a practice advocated by some), the time must come when it must be backed. If it has worn a roller or a saddle without stirrup irons during its training, then it will be used to this and to being girthed up, which is usually more objectionable to a pony than having the saddle on its back. A sack of straw with a little sand or gravel at each end to help it stay in place on the saddle is helpful in getting the pony used to having more than a saddle on its back, though the average Shetland does not care what is put on its back, provided, in a young pony, that it is not too heavy. If a lightweight girl or boy who can ride is gently put up, it is almost certain that the pony will walk away with the rider as if it had been doing it for years. But one must be prepared for eventualities and a mistake at this stage in training might mean a great deal more work and trouble.

The following illustration from Shetland shows just how little the average Shetland minds being backed. Here breeding mares are not normally handled much. In this case, however, the mares were quiet, well handled and used to being led. The owners were showing two visitors the mares and their foals. With the visitors was a small girl who had never ridden a pony. The four adults were engrossed in observing and discussing the ponies when turning round they were astonished to see the small girl astride a young mare who had her foal beside her but had never been backed. In addition, to make the pony move the child was giving her a smack on the quarters and never did that pony show any resentment. Later on the same child scrambled up on a three year old mare with her first foal at foot: though this one was not quite so amenable she made no attempt to get rid of the girl.

If the pony is to be driven the initial training is the same but instead of, or in addition to, being backed the pony must learn to be put to a vehicle and pull it.

First of all it is best to get the pony used to a blinker bridle though some people prefer to use an open one for driving. This does not take long and the long reining can be done while it is on. It is advisable not to drive the pony over rough ground, to keep away from noises and sounds that might startle him, and not to give sudden touches as it must be remembered that until the blinkers went on he was seeing everything that was going on around. Here, too, the voice is a great help. Once the pony is used to blinkers the rest of the harness should be put on – that is collar or breast collar and breeching. After a day or two with this on the traces should be used by either fixing a light stick to them, or a piece of cord which the handler can hold or, if an assistant is available, a longer cord which the assistant holds and by pulling or easing it varies the pressure on the pony's shoulders. Provided all is going well it is useful at the same time for a light branch or some sticks to be dragged along: this accustoms the pony to the continual and changing noises behind him which a vehicle will make. The average Shetland pony will quickly learn these lessons and will be ready to be put to in a matter of a few days. The actual putting to must be done with care and it is advisable to have two assistants if possible, one at the pony's head and one at each side. The pony should be led to start with, the driver walking on the offside using the reins. The pony should be helped in starting off, in stopping and when turning by the assistant who, taking a shaft should either push or pull gently so that the animal has not got to do everything himself. Probably after a few turns and a little walking around the driver may get in the vehicle, but it is as well to have someone very near to hold the pony's head should anything go wrong, for this could be disastrous. During all these preparations and exercises it is essential that the voice is used not only to give commands such as 'Walk' or 'Whoa' but words of encouragement, though naturally it is not the words themselves that count but the tone of the voice in which they are said.

The driving of Shetlands in a team, pairs or single is no innovation. There are illustrations of these ponies in harness in the past and also quite a few recordings of driving by some owners during the present century. The Ladies Estella and Dorothea Hope owned the $35\frac{1}{2}''$ mare Hoplemuroma who was not only an excellent breeding mare but also did exceptionally well in harness. She is said to have trotted four miles in sixteen minutes, seven miles in twenty-nine minutes and nine miles in forty-three minutes. Ridden by a four stone boy and given 300 yards start, she won a trotting handicap in a class for 14 h.h. and under. The Ladies Hope with a 37″ pair drove eleven miles in sixty-five minutes.

More than one source relates that a Shetland mare 'Beauty', owned by a Mr R. Lacy, trotted ten miles in thirty-nine minutes thirty seconds while being driven by a man weighing 11 st 4 lbs. This mare had frequently travelled a mile in three minutes forty-four seconds.

Now that driving marathons and three day events are more frequent more figures will no doubt be forthcoming, but it has already been shown that these ponies can compete successfully with horses in harness when the latter are suitably handicapped or allowances made for the Shetlands' shorter stride.

My wife regularly drove a pair of 37″ stallions before the war and with three persons in the phaeton would cover seven miles of extremely hilly road in well under the hour. Lady Estella took a pair of chestnut stallions to the Aachen show in the 1930s and had some successes.

In the early years of this century Mrs Wentworth Hope Johnstone drove a team and although records are rather vague it seems that other

Author and gelding Twist of Marshwood returning to Main Ring at Royal Show, Stonelegh, after 6 mile marathon

teams were in use as well. In the period between the wars a number of owners were regularly driving Shetlands and there were classes for them at some shows. The International Horse Show, then held in Olympia, put on a class for single harness when six or eight entries came forward, mostly to show waggons being driven around the flower decked arena. One year a lady driver failed to balance correctly while cornering and left the waggon rather hurriedly and not as gracefully as she might have wished.

Mrs Ducker, also, had a good team on the road. Others who drove were Lady Hunloke, Lady Hobart, Mrs Atkinson, Mrs M. Cox and others at home and in smaller shows.

An anonymous owner of Shetland ponies writing to the *Bazaar* in January 1926 might well be quoted here as she corroborates the opinion of many other owners. This lady owner had a 41″ mare which she got down from Shetland. She writes

'My children all learnt to ride on her, she taught them a good deal and now my grandchildren are receiving instructions from her and she herself at twenty-three years of age is just as full of life

and vigour and her legs as clean and straight as when I first extrac-
ted her – for a long time I drove her regularly and found her
an excellent trapper. I took her into Devonshire where the natives
at first scoffed at the idea of a pony of that size on their hills.
I had not been there long before one of them remarked that she
went up the St Peter's hill better than any other horse in the
parish! During the nineteen years I have had her she has never
been sick or sorry.'

The same owner relates how she had another wonderful pony, a
39″ chocolate chestnut stallion: 'When 24 years old he covered
his mile in four minutes with three adults in the trap'. She tells that
she owns a daughter of this stallion which is equally good and also a
piebald stallion which she has been driving for ten years. 'He has never
yet been touched with the whip and no day is too long for him.' The
article ends: 'I will conclude by quoting an old saying I have heard
about them, namely, that for its size the "Sheltie" is the best horse-
flesh in the world.'

Other owners and witnesses (including experts) could be quoted
on the staunch and willing character of the Shetland.

In the article in *The Field* in June 1920 recalling the feats of
Hoplemuroma, Sir William Day, the author of *Racehorse in Training*
and an authority, is quoted as having said

'It is singular that such gameness as well as physical power of
endurance should be so frequently evinced by the smallest sort
of horse than comparatively the larger. Yet that it is so is an
indisputable fact.'

It is gratifying to see the increase in both riding and driving classes
for Shetlands at many shows and to see entries in open pony classes
as well. The Stud Book Society presents rosettes for the best Shetland
in the latter in an effort to encourage the entries. Entries in the riding
and driving classes frequently exceed single figures thus demon-
strating the popularity not only of these ponies but of these com-
petitions, although unfortunately there is less support in the north
and the standard of entry is not so high.

In the late nineteenth century and up to about the 1930s a number
of Shetland ponies were used at large Spas, health resorts and seaside

towns for drawing Bath-chairs. These comfortably upholstered, often coach-built, four wheeled vehicles were on hire for invalids, convalescents and sometimes the victims of over-indulgence to enable them to get fresh air and to meet or greet others. Either Shetlands or donkeys were used but the former were the most popular and frequent. Whilst the chair was occupied by the hirer, the 'boy', often a grown man, walked alongside driving or leading the pony; but when returning to stables at the end of their day a smart trot, with the boy sitting in the chair, was the general rule. Many of the ponies for this task were bought at regular horse and pony sales in neighbouring market towns: their price was usually £4 to £10. All the ponies were shod at a cost of 1/6d a set or just over. Occasionally a client would buy the pony which had been pulling the chair, probably for a grandchild to ride and drive. Then, as now, beach ponies were popular in seaside towns and here again Shetlands formed quite a large proportion of the available rides.

Anyone who has attended a few circuses must have seen Shetland ponies performing in the ring and eliciting applause and appreciation.

Pit pony being groomed – Ahington colliery

This popular use has made them well-known in countries far from their native islands.

It has already been mentioned how popular and adaptable they were for the coal mines. Although in the early days stabling and underground conditions were poor, these were later improved and it is doubtful if any working horse or pony had better feeding and stabling conditions. Furthermore, the horsekeepers who looked after them were devoted to their charges and took great pride in them. Now few ponies are employed underground for the mines have been mechanised and animal drawn transport is not required.

Whilst on the subject of these ponies in harness work their widespread use in Holland for all forms of work should be mentioned. Scarcely a farm or horticultural holding was without one or two Shetland ponies who did much agricultural work from hauling the milk to harrowing and rolling. The Shetland pony's work on agricultural and horticultural holdings was considered so important that the Dutch Government carried out carefully planned and executed Achievement Tests in 1956. As a result it was found that the Shetland pony had tractive power of 42.8% of body weight as against 27.6% of the huge Belgian horse. Tests also proved the correctness of Lord Londonderry's stud managers in aiming for small heavy ponies for they showed that the smaller, thicker animal had greater draught pulling potentialities.

In East Germany tests on similar lines were also carried out. It was found that the Shetland pony when starting to move and when drawing heavy loads pulls directly forward, whilst a horse is inclined to lower its forehand.

In this connection Bryner Jones has a very interesting comment:

'From his extraordinary power for his inches the Shetland Pony has been called a Clydesdale horse in miniature. This is a misnomer, except as regards their wonderful weight-shifting power.'

Now as in many other spheres, mechanisation has taken over most of these tasks.

One unusual task which was apparently enjoyed by both pony and rider, was the carrying of the huntsman of a pack of foxhounds at a

Sergeant Ringway: this thirteen-year old Shetland pony is the official mascot of the Parachute Regiment

hound exercise during a late summer in the war, when Charlie Gosden used a Shetland gelding which had been given to his daughter a few years before as her first pony.

The use of these ponies for disabled and handicapped children is quite common and the organisations endorse the use of well-trained Shetlands.

There must be few tasks that a Shetland pony has not done. The Argyll and Sutherland Highlanders had as their mascot for a number of years a stallion bred by a former Commanding Officer and his wife and there is at least one unit of the Army which now has such a pony. Years ago a Shetlander on business in Central Europe observed a band and procession marching along a street headed by a small Shetland pony.

They are found in Zoos and Public parks, in the children's pet corner giving children confidence and a liking for animals. Of course they are well known in the hunting field, and there are some excellent performers amongst them; many a determined child has had grand hunts, crawling where the fence has been too formidable.

At Pony Club rallies they make regular appearances and at least two (probably many more), have accomplished the Pony Club Elementary Dressage Test.

In Norway there are held well organised and conducted races with children as jockeys. No doubt in other countries more and diverse occupations may be found for them.

The magazine now produced by the Stud Book Society, edited so successfully by Mrs R. A. B. Gosling during its formative years, gives members information about shows – not only the dates of those to be held but results of the judging – as well as much other information concerning the breed.

It seems that in 1926, so that members might be kept in touch with events in the Society, an arrangement was made with the *Bazaar Exchange and Mart* that information provided by the Secretary would be published every fortnight in the *Bazaar*. In those days the paper had an agricultural section containing articles and some show results. This arrangement appears to have come to a fairly abrupt conclusion when the Secretary wrote to the publishers enquiring why certain material sent had not been published as arranged. He received a polite reply pointing out that the excerpts from a book (presumably Vol. I of the Stud Book) had been published thirty five years ago 'and the matter in it can hardly be considered up-to-date. Possibly, too, the members of your Society and others interested in the Shetland, also have the book, and would hardly look upon extracts from it as interesting.'

A few more items were contributed before the arrangement ceased entirely.

My wife and I have always tried to put into practice what we preached about the Shetland pony being a general purpose pony and very many ponies have left the Marshwood stud trained for children and for driving. We have both driven horses, cobs and Shetland ponies for years and both of us wish that we could do much more of it now. There are two main reasons why we do not: one is the frightening amount of heavy, fast traffic on the roads and the second is the lack of skilled assistance which is necessary. Neither of us have the time to turn out, clean and sparkling as they must be, the pony, harness and vehicle. When we lived at Marshwood Manor Betty used to drive a pair of greys and later a pair of black stallions to a park phaeton. She often returned social calls in this way within a radius of eight or ten miles and at times did some local shopping as well as driving to horse shows or sports in the neighbourhood.

We bred and trained the pair of Shetlands that were driven by Dame Anna Neagle to Queen Victoria's phaeton in the film *Victoria the Great*. In 1939 we had hopes of putting a black four-in-hand of Shetlands on the road, but Hitler stopped that. We used a Shetland for various carting jobs about the place including carting out the stable muck, sometimes with a single pony and sometimes a tandem. We used both two and four wheeled vehicles and often thought of having a sleigh, but never found one or had one made of the right size.

# 8

# *Showing*

How much to show and where must cause some concern to those new-comers inexperienced in this sphere.

Showing, for some people, becomes a chronic habit and they feel that under no circumstances must they miss any show within a certain radius or one of a certain size or status. Therefore much of their time is spent at shows or preparing for them and travelling to and fro, which may well be a full day's journey.

It is perfectly true that some shows are of benefit to the breed. It is only natural that the breed should have a 'shop window', and many breeders feel that this is an excellent opportunity to place their goods before the public.

In the south-west of the country, before the war, not many shows had classes for Shetland ponies, unlike today when there are numerous opportunities to exhibit. Neither were there as many ponies as there are now: probably in the 1920s there were not more than five or six breeders of Shetland ponies in all the south-west of England. So there was little inducement for smaller shows to include Shetland classes. I sometimes wonder whether today the number of shows is not excessive, though I presume that if the classes are reasonably well filled the holding of the show is fully justifiable.

The Bath and West show always kept classes for Shetlands, but I must say once or twice it was touch and go whether they could be included in the schedule because of low entries. It may not always have been one of the best shows to attend, but in our opinion it is now certainly one of the most pleasant shows at which to exhibit ponies.

Another show to which my wife usually sent ponies was the National Pony Show at the Agricultural Hall in Islington which was always held in March. I recall that the principal classes and most exhibits were those for Polo pony breeding and young stock and that Shetland and Welsh ponies were the two native breeds that were always represented, woolly coats and all.

There were one or two shows of County standard which included a class for Shetlands, but usually it was only by exhibiting in First Pony or Leading Rein classes that the Shetlands could come before the public at most shows in the south of England before the war.

What tremendous differences are apparent when one compares the shows of today with those of say thirty-five or forty years ago! At the really large shows, such as the Royal, Highland and Bath and West, until about 1935 most of the stock (horses and ponies included) arrived and departed by rail. They arrived at the nearest station by railway horse box and in many cases continued on to the showground in a railway owned horsedrawn float.

It sometimes seems that there are too many shows at present. I do not believe that a prolificity of small events of this kind really benefits the breed; if one compares the number of Shetland ponies in the country with the number shown, only an infinitesimal proportion come before the Society's judges.

The show organisers must give all entrants equal consideration and help, ensure that rules and regulations are properly carried out and adhered to and that no doubtful or unfair practices are allowed. There should never be any suspicion of unfair or prejudicial treatment.

During the last few years the number of shows has greatly increased and so also have Shetland classes at shows which previously did not include them in their schedule or prize list. So great is the increase that perhaps the many opportunities to exhibit one's stock have given rise to a kind of showing fever. In some areas without travelling far it would be easy to have pony exhibits at two or more shows on the same day during some of the summer show season. It seems that many ponies meet the same opponents at different shows and as likely as not a judge may have to place the same exhibits several times during the season.

These shows are fun and competitors enjoy them: they meet friends and their friends' ponies; they gossip and pass remarks about other competitors and, of course, the judge is not neglected. But seriously, are these little shows of much value to the breed? It is doubtful. The exhibitors all know each other and their ponies and the gate is not big; the spectators for the most part are only interested in their own breed or classes and pay little or no attention to others.

I am not condemning or deprecating the holding of shows but saying that their standard should be raised. It is good for the breed that many of its supporters are willing to attend these shows and prepare their ponies for them, because even at the small functions the exhibits must be in reasonably good condition. One would like to think that all prizewinners at shows reached a certain standard of excellence, but it must be admitted that sometimes in a badly filled class it is difficult to reconcile the quality of the prize winners with a First, Second or even Third prize. Judges may refuse to award a prize to an animal he or she considers to be below standard, but this is not an easy decision to make.

Unst pony show

In advertisements or particulars given of a pony for sale one sometimes reads that it has been awarded a Championship or many First prizes. When one makes enquiries, as one certainly should, as to where these awards were won, it may be learnt that the championship was awarded at the Slowcombe-under-Moor Rotary Club's Bi-annual Show and the First Prizes gained at the Nether Smack-em-down Church Fête. These statements of winnings can be misleading to newcomers to the breed, whereas those who have been breeding and exhibiting or watching show results will suspect that they are of minor importance as the names will not have cropped up in the summaries of past shows. Encouragement to show is excellent but the quality of the exhibit must be seriously taken into consideration.

There are far more breeders of Shetland ponies who do not show than who do and they cannot advertise the numerous wins and successes of their stock: this does not mean, however, that their ponies are inferior to the award winners. Not all breeders are prepared to go on exhibiting year in year out at many shows, nor can they spare the time for preparation and absence from home. Others are not sufficiently interested in showing to do so at all. Moreover, there are many keen, interested owners who would be delighted to put some of their animals before the public but are unable to do so because they have children or an invalid to be cared for, or there is some other reason which prevents them.

Any new breeder or owner starting to show should first realise that much as he would like to win, it is highly unlikely that he will always be successful. He must be prepared to take defeat generously and without rancour. When a judge considers that someone else has a better pony the loser should take the decision in good grace. After all, the top judges of stock do not always see eye to eye and their preferences may differ slightly.

Exhibitors and spectators are sometimes apt to forget that the judge should judge a pony by its actual performance in the ring and this has been known to be overlooked by judges, also, before now. An exhibitor, now deceased, had a very good pony which quite rightly won numerous prizes but towards the end of a show season was showing very definite signs of staleness. The handler was inclined to assume that as long as the pony was in the ring it would automatically be brought in first. One judge did not agree with this assumption: the pony was stale and not showing itself at all. The judge pulled ponies in as he fancied them and this well-known prize winner was left walking round with some others while the judge considered which he would pull in next. This was too much for the owner. He stalked into the ring and demanded of the judge if he knew what he was doing as this wonderful animal had won everywhere else. The judge replied that he was well aware which pony it was and that he intended placing it just where he thought it should be.

Any owner who shows will hear sooner or later all sorts of stories and gossip which he would be wise to ignore for it is almost impossible for everyone in a class to be completely satisfied. Even if happy in the place the judge has allotted, he may quite unlikely feel that one or two other exhibits in the class should have been higher or lower.

If the decision to show is taken, then the exhibitor must start preparing the pony for show; but if there is a doubt as to whether the pony is good enough to compete it is advisable to seek expert advice before commencing preparation. It must be said that even if the pony is not quite good enough to get 'into the money' there is excitement and a spirit of adventure in a first attempt at showing, particularly if the show is of some importance.

It used to be firmly believed by those who showed ponies or horses that the first essential, provided that the animal had sufficient merit to be shown at all, was that it was fit. This belief has suffered somewhat among Shetland ponies and other breeds, for many ponies shown have excessive flesh which prevents the judge from seeing the frame of the animal and also much handicaps the action of the pony. It seems that the showing of ponies in too fat a condition is not altogether something new, for Douglas writes:

'Every good horse ought to suggest to the imagination the general structure of his bony framework; and it ought scarcely to be possible to conceal this by any reasonable degree of condition, or to bring about, in a horse, a general appearance of bonelessness such as might be proper to the carcase of a perfectly fattened Aberdeen-Angus bullock. It should not be forgotten by breeders or judges that a pony whose shoulders, hips and stifles

are not prominent in his appearance, is either defective in
structure or very improperly overfed.'
From observations made at many shows it always appears that the
Shetland classes contain the worst offenders in this respect, frequently generating well deserved criticism for their overweight
condition.

In the past there were weeks of preparation before a stallion or colt
was taken to a show. He might have two hours or more walking exercise a day, being lunged or trotted out in a ring, track or circular
manège, but in addition to this he was strapped really thoroughly
every day after his exercise, having been quartered before going out.
Nowadays it may not be possible to be quite so thorough, but some
attempt towards such a goal should be made, even if time and skill
are scarce. Time, unless one has an assistant, is a scarce commodity
these days with all the other commitments that arise; but it has been
said – quite rightly – that one should never keep more animals than
can be confidently looked after in the way which they should be. If
the time cannot be spared to give him adequate walking exercise, at
least some time every day should be spared to lunge the stallion. It is
essential that he is properly lunged and this matter is discussed in
another chapter.

Strapping is now almost an unknown art amongst many who breed
and exhibit ponies. One only has to walk round the boxes at a show to
see some of the most pathetic efforts at strapping; it seems that it is
either not taught to those starting work in stables, or no one bothers
to insist that it is done properly. Some really terrible examples have
been seen: heavy jerseys or even jackets are kept on in some cases
when, if the job is being done correctly and vigorously, sweat is
pouring off without a jersey. Possibly the supreme effort was the
girl who after fifteen years in a stable did not bother to take off her
anorak!!

Poor or infrequent strapping results in the pony not being as
clean as he should be. This brings up the doubtfully beneficial
habit of washing ponies. The pony should be produced at the show
clean, the time available for attending to the ponies may be limited and
strapping takes time; so the alternative method of cleaning is to
wash them. Some exhibitors do not seem to realise that a pony has a

natural grease which is clean and puts the bloom and shine on its jacket. This is why a well-strapped pony has such a bloom for the ducts in the skin are stimulated by the strapping and the natural grease is exuded to bring the shine. If the pony is washed the soap or detergent removes this grease altogether so the bloom disappears. This allows the coat or jacket to stand away from the skin thus giving the coat a woolly or 'stivery' appearance instead of a smooth glossy one. All the concoctions that are used – from hair cream and toilet paraffin to black shoe polish – cannot really replace the natural grease. Should circumstances be such that ponies have to be washed, it must be done at least three days before the show to allow sufficient time for some of the natural oil or grease to return to the coat, and it must be encouraged to do so, with possibly only twenty minutes wisping twice a day. If the exhibitor decides that this procedure is not possible it would be advisable to cut down the entries and concentrate on fewer animals.

The washing of a Shetland pony's tail and mane is rather a different matter. For unless the pony has been stabled and groomed continuously, these may well need washing as the Shetlands' massive growth of hair makes it difficult to clean thoroughly without the use of water. However, here again it should be done a few days before the show, and care taken to wash only the mane and tail. It is important to thoroughly rinse the hair as soap or detergent left on the skin or in the hair can cause intense irritation and subsequent blemishes.

I do not intend to describe or explain the practice or art of proper grooming. It is fully detailed in many books on horses and ponies and most children should receive lessons at Pony Club rallies if they have not already learnt it at home. However, the practice of wisping does appear to be neglected although it is a splendid method of helping to get an animal fit and bring a good natural bloom to the coat. It is doubtful if many know how to make a wisp and use it correctly. Possibly many of those without much experience do not realise that the feeding of a pony or horse affects the amount of grease and scurf which an animal secretes in its coat and a change in the diet can make a great difference.

It is natural that owners of ponies which are to be shown should feed them so that their charges are looking their best. However, it is not just a question of putting this mixture or that into the trough or feed tin for feeding: to get the very best results is an art. One used to hear the term or description of a 'good feeder' or a 'very good feeder' when one spoke of a groom or other person who had charge of stock, but this has probably nearly gone out of use. It meant that the groom really studied how and what the animals ate, how much they thrived on one mixture more than another and so on. Some ponies will not touch one kind of food whilst others may wire into it: the good feeder sees that correct mixing of different ingredients will make a pony or horse eat and thrive.

It is most important that the pony is fed at regular times and this should always be the case when feeding ponies whether they are out at grass or are in stables. For ponies that are stabled and being prepared for show, the total daily feed should be given in four feeds if possible. These should be at regular intervals, always at the same time, the first reasonably early in the morning, the last after straightening out the stables fairly late in the evening.

The secret of success in conditioning horses and ponies is to feed them little and often. It is essential to have clean feeding buckets, tins or mangers and fresh water in a clean bucket or other container should always be available for drinking.

The pony, after being exercised and groomed, should be given every opportunity to rest and be disturbed as little as possible. Droppings should always be removed from the box and bedding at any time provided the pony is not disturbed for that purpose. A skep or similar article should be kept handy for this use.

The other preparations for showing the pony are training for the show, and the tack. Unfortunately the training for the show ring is often insufficient: this is not only a mistake which could make a pony lower in its class than it need have been but it also is not very complimentary to the judge or the show. It is essential that every entrant should have been taught how to lead and stand and will do these things correctly whenever asked. There can be exceptional circumstances, but these are rare. A crowd and many other ponies around are no excuse for an exhibit not to lead both at walk and trot or stand quietly if the training has been thorough for in ninety-nine cases out of a hundred a pony will behave as it has been taught. It takes time and patience, but a pony worth showing is worth showing properly.

The pony must be taught to walk and trot freely on a loose rein: it should on no account pull or lean on its leader and from a freely moving walk it should break into a trot when the leader drops his hand and says the word. It must be taught to stand correctly on all four legs, not to fidget or move away when the judge puts his hand on it, nor to lift its feet unless it receives the office to do so should the judge run his hand down a leg or feel for bone. Nothing looks worse than an exhibitor trying to get a reluctant, partly trained animal to walk or trot, ineffectually flapping the spare end of a too long rein with the left hand round behind him, or waving a long cutting whip trying to connect with the pony's quarters but in fact making him even worse. Many exhibitors, also, turn their pony the wrong way round at the end of their walk or trot. Always turn the pony right about; there are two good reasons: firstly, the judge wants to see the pony turn not the exhibitor, which happens if the leader swings the pony round himself instead of walking round the pony, and secondly anyone turning the incorrect way with a very fresh animal, particularly something larger than a Shetland, may receive a very unpleasant cow kick from their charge.

The question of tack for showing is very important and can make a great difference to the appearance of a pony in the ring.

It is not at all easy nowadays to find really first class leather but with some trouble a pony owner can discover good quality material. Normally yearlings of either sex, and two year old fillies, are best shown in a neatly fitting leather headcollar. Not only should it fit nicely but it should also be of lightweight leather and a thin leather lead rein buckled on to the back 'D' of the head collar looks better than a headrope. For older ponies it is usual, though not essential, to use a bridle and bit, and if there is any question of the handler not being able to control or hold the pony, most certainly it should have a bit in its mouth.

However, it is worse than useless to use a bit if the pony is not accustomed to one, for it will fidget, fret and obviously will not show itself to advantage. Therefore, if a pony is to have a bit in its mouth at a show it must get used to this sometime previously. A jointed snaffle is probably the best bit with which to start: it should fit well into the corners of the mouth without wrinkling the skin so that there is no chance of encouraging the pony to get its tongue over by having it too low in the mouth. The bit should be used when exercising the pony and may be left in the mouth for fifteen to twenty minutes whilst in a box or stable. The lead rein should not be attached to the ring of the bit but to the back of the noseband. It may well be found that this attachment is all that is required at a show and that it is not necessary to use the bit at all. For actual showing some exhibitors much prefer a straight bar snaffle and if it is intended to use one the pony should have the opportunity of becoming accustomed to it. Here again the bridle should be neat, well-made and must fit the pony's head: it does not look good if the noseband is hanging down almost over the nostrils or the browband is too big. Coloured browbands may be fitted, but a plain leather one is really most suitable. There should be no decoration on the bridle except, perhaps, a plain brass rosette or disc where the browband fits the headpiece.

During the twenties and thirties the fitting of rollers or surcingles on stallions was widespread amongst Shetland stallion exhibitors and as well as side reins it was quite usual to see bearing reins in use. Now, however, probably most stallions and colts are shown without such tack.

If tack is to be worn it must be tidy, well-made and, above all, it must be correctly put on for if it is not this can greatly detract from a pony's appearance. It should be realised that to fit the roller to show a pony at its best is an art. Everything has to be just right: the roller must not be too tight or too loose, the side reins must be the right length and above all the roller must be in the right place to show off a colt to his best advantage. Furthermore the colt or stallion must be thoroughly trained and absolutely in control otherwise the very best fitted tack may be misplaced. If the colt or stallion is fat it is almost impossible to fit the roller to stay in the correct position or, if it is tightened up enough to keep it so, unsightly rolls of fat protrude before and behind.

Naturally the exhibitor will keep the bridle and other tack clean and supple and the brass well polished. For those who have to buy new tack it is well worth darkening the leather before using it at a show as a light coloured, obviously new bridle or headcollar detracts from a pony's appearance. An old but effective method of darkening leather was to wash it well and then soak it in strong tea, but today effective leather stains are on the market. At one time quite a few colts and stallions were shown in white leather and webbing tack but this is not attractive and the novice exhibitor is strongly advised not to use anything but brown leather.

Exhibitors must pay attention all the time they are in the ring and be ready to do immediately whatever the ring steward requests of them. At all times, whilst before the judge, they should be presenting and showing off their pony and standing in front of it. One sees too often exhibitors standing as if half asleep, consequently their charges are standing just anyhow and if the judge looks down the line as many often do, the impression given by the exhibit could be detrimental to the final placing. Constant attention should be paid for exhibitors may well gain knowledge and experience by careful observation of the other ponies and the 'coffee-housing' should be left until out of the ring. It is only good manners to the judge and officials to be attentive and polite. It may be difficult sometimes to be grateful but the judge and stewards do their best and their word should be accepted with good grace.

Nothing yet has been said about the personal dress of exhibitors but many of the public, show organisers and the judges do expect to see handlers or leaders of ponies neatly turned out. Finally, do make certain that you have all your tack, buckets, tickets and so on before leaving home and leave in plenty of time, as one never knows what delays might occur en route. It is embarrassing to arrive late for a class and may lead to disappointment.

Having discussed shows from an exhibitor's point of view let us look at them from that of a judge.

Judges are appointed onto the panel by the Council of the Society, a member of which recommends that the name be added. So the Council assume that the nominator, and possibly one or two other members who know the proposed, are confident that he or she will make a satisfactory judge. The proposed judge can, of course, refuse on the grounds of insufficient experience of ponies or some other reason. It is easy enough to accept this appointment. However the first few shows for the judge, faced with a number of ponies whose owners realise it is his first attempt and probably know as much as him if not more, can be awkward and nerve-racking.

The judge must give his or her unbiased opinion in the placing of the ponies. It is irrelevant if a pony has won at previous shows for it only matters how the ponies are at the present moment of judging. It does not matter who the pony belongs to or who bred it; the judge's job is to put the ponies in what he or she considers honestly to be the correct order. Sometimes one sees the judge talking to someone at the ringside; this is not really correct behaviour for the judge should only talk to stewards of his ring or show officials after classes are completed.

Judges should make certain from their stewards exactly what is the class to be judged for some shows, particularly smaller ones, have mixed classes which can be confusing unless thoroughly explained. They should never show preference for colour: it is the conformation, breed type and action which they have to judge. Nor should too much stress be placed on height for a very good small pony could well be placed above some of the not so good bigger ones.

Regrettably exhibitors have been known to try and influence the judge in the ring. An exhibitor was heard to tell the judge that his pony had won at 'so and so' and 'so and so' shows. Under the circumstances the exhibitor was lucky to have his pony placed bottom (it was a very nice pony) instead of finding themselves outside the ring. But judges, also, can ask or say unwise things, which possibly they afterwards regret, such as asking a handler whose pony it was that she led. These unfortunate lapses always cause widespread indignation and get spread around. No judge should ever lay himself open to the least suspicion of dishonesty or preference, nor should he ever consult a catalogue before or during judging (either his own or that belonging to anyone else); nor should he linger whilst passing the pony stables or lines.

After the conclusion of judging, perhaps after the judge has had a drink or a meal, if he or she can spare the time to go round the pony lines or amongst the trailers and horse boxes to meet some of the exhibitors, this gesture is generally appreciated. It gives owners the chance to ask the judge what he did or did not like about their ponies and to discuss various other matters concerning their animals. It is unfair, however, to suggest to a judge that ponies owned by others are not as good or that he or she made a grave mistake.

Of course no pony bred by the judge or one which was sold to the exhibitor by the judge should ever be put before him.

There was a time in this country when Shetland pony classes were occasionally judged by two judges, as is usually the case in Continental countries and frequently, of course, in Hunter classes here. If the judges do not agree about a decision this can cause much delay.

In Holland all mares and their foals are brought to shows, inspected and classified into I, II or III Premiums every year. At the subsequent stallion shows the quality of each exhibit's progeny is taken into account before any awards are made; thus if a very good looking stallion is not leaving foals of any merit he will not feature high in the final placings. A practice which might be of interest to exhibitors in this country is one in use in Sweden and Denmark. With the judge in the ring one steward has the special task of jotting down on a pad of duplicate forms the judge's comments on every pony exhibited. These comments are of necessity brief probably mentioning a pony's worst fault such as 'Coarse and bad action' or perhaps of a good animal, 'Lot of quality, good mover'. One copy of the comments is handed to the exhibitor before leaving the ring: thus he or she is aware immediately of what the judge considered to be merits or failings of the pony.

Showing one's ponies was once about the only way to keep one's name and ponies before the public. Now, however, the Society's Magazine and possibility of advertising in various periodicals devoted to horses and ponies has made the need to do so less urgent.

# 9

# *Exports*

It is impossible to guess or state when and how the first export of ponies was made from the Shetland Isles. It may have been that a Viking raider decided to take some back with him to Scandinavia but there are all sorts of other possibilities.

However it is probable that some were shipped to Holland and to Hamburg in the seventeenth century. The Dutch fishing fleet spent a great deal of time in the waters off Shetland and used the islands as their base to some extent. It is recorded that whilst ashore some of the fishermen rode the ponies for exercise. So it surely stands to reason that a few of them found their way across the North Sea in a Dutch fishing boat, whilst ships were crossing fairly frequently to Hamburg as this port had a lively trade with Shetland.

In addition to this possible trade directly with the islands, ponies must have been brought down to ports in Scotland and England from time to time in trading vessels.

The first authenticated consignment of ponies to leave the islands for a foreign country is one of seventy-five imported by Eli Elliot in the U.S.A. in 1885. Two years later this same buyer again crossed the Atlantic and returned with a further consignment of 129, this being the largest ever single lot to be exported. These ponies were used for children to ride and as driving ponies.

The Shetland Pony Stud Book Society's volumes do not carry any detail of exports until 1907 when the names of members who exported and buyers are recorded. In the 1906 volume there is a list of 420 ponies for which certificates had been issued but no details are given about exporters or their destination. Dr Elliot of Bedford, Mass., estimated that in 1906 there were approximately 5000 of the breed in the U.S.A.

In the ten years 1905–14 a total of 2150 Shetland ponies were exported, the majority by Shetland men, in particular Anderson Manson and John Anderson and Sons from Hillswick in the north of Mainland. In addition it seems that a certain number of non-registered ponies were shipped. In 1911 the Shetland Islands Stud Book was formed with the express purpose of being able to grant certificates of export to ponies which had not been registered with the original Society. Although the U.S.A. authorities refused to recognise the certificates issued by the Society, the Government of Canada did agree and consequently many left Shetland for there. It is of interest to read the introduction in the Shetland Islands' Stud Book:

> 'There has not been much demand for Shetland ponies for the American market during the past year. Very few ponies have been bought for America and the circumstances are such that it may be some time before ponies are wanted in any considerable number for that purpose. At present the owners and breeders in the U.S.A. hold large stocks of Shetland ponies – partly imported, and partly bred in the U.S.A. – and until these stocks are considerably reduced it is not expected that there will be much increase in the exports to America.'

The American Shetland Pony Club was founded in 1888 and published their first Stud Book in 1893. The height limit is no less than 46″ and the type of pony bred now is very different from the true Shetland type. It is described as the 'refined or improved American type' and it is difficult to understand how such a pony has been bred from pure, true type Shetland ponies. Eli Elliot, already mentioned, was one of the founder members of this Pony Club. He had been to Shetland and had imported some ponies so he must have gained some knowledge of the pony to be found in the islands. He wrote in a book:

'I never saw in any country, what I believe to be a "right

Shetland" that was as much as 46″ high. As long as I can get them straight in the legs and round in the body they cannot be too small.'

Amongst the many imported was 'a pony 31″ and full grown'.

It is interesting to find that Charles E. Bunn who became a President of the American Shetland Pony Club corroborates this statement in a booklet he published. He writes,

'– and of all breeds of ponies the Shetland is the smallest, the most gentle, the freest from defect, the most able to stand neglect and the easiest to keep. ... I personally do not believe any purebred Shetland ever attains the height of 46″. ... I am often asked for a 48″ to 50″ Shetland. I wish to state emphatically, no such animal exists. ... Many ponies are called Shetlands which possess no characteristic of the breed whatsoever.'

There can be no doubt that the large demand from across the Atlantic as well as that within the United Kingdom was almost causing a shortage of ponies. Dr Elliot mentions this and quotes a letter he had received from a large dealer in the islands: '... good aged mares I cannot obtain. Can furnish you with colts but aged mares of the quality you require are not to be had'. In addition he cites the London Livestock Almanac of 1907 where a Mr John Hill writes of two of the largest dealers on the islands buying Shetlands in England:

'When the Shetland breeders are coming to the Mainland to buy it indicates very clearly the studs there have been pretty well depleted which we know is the case and the prospects for Shelties are very good, and there is no difficulty in getting £15 for the commonest filly of pedigree while anything of merit may bring any figure.'

Information on the price Americans were paying for ponies is very sketchy but the £15 mentioned does seem to be about an average price for a two or three year old filly, whilst £50 is the price quoted for an exported stallion. However the prices paid in the U.S.A. are quoted: 'A good looking Shetland, guaranteed safe and well broken for the use of children, will easily bring $200–250 on the Chicago market today.' It is not always clear whether the amounts the ponies

Lerwick from the breakwater, earlier this century

fetch are for imported or home bred ones, though Dr Bunn writes
that a stallion of his breeding fetched $1000 at an auction in Ohio.
The dollar at that time was worth approximately four shillings.

Apparently the cost of shipment was about $60 – say £12–£15 –
per head and should the animal have an export certificate showing
three generations of registered ponies the duty was $30. At one time
an authority in the U.S.A. stated that 'Most of the registered ponies
have been exported and there are now but few left and these high

in price'. On referring to our Stud Book for those years this statement is shown to be hardly correct; but no doubt, in view of the large number already sold, breeders were holding on to their remaining mares and fillies or, if prepared to sell, were making the most of a sellers' market.

The Shetland pony has always been extremely popular in the U.S.A., but its present form in that continent bears little resemblance to the true type pony as we know it. The final lines of an article written at the end of the century about this American pony might help to explain the great difference:

> 'In fact some Shetlands display quite remarkable knee action and fold their feet under them with the sharp precision of a veteran high stepper. In fact, the Shetland of today is sloughing off his crudities that passed off unnoticed among the foothills of his bleak Island home of earlier days'!

A report of Illinois State Fair in the *Breeders' Gazette* of approximately sixty years ago states,

> 'It was of especial interest to note that recently imported ponies contrasted quite unfavourably as to quality with the ponies which have been carefully bred to showyard type for some years in this country.

After the 1914–18 war fewer Shetland ponies were exported to the U.S.A. and until 1953 not many were taken over the Atlantic. It was then that the demand grew and once more American and Canadian buyers came over to procure Shetlands.

Owing to the comparative lack of demand in this country, both prior to the war and during wartime, fewer had been bred and the number of registered mares and fillies available for sale was strictly limited. However, in the years 1953–60 around 360 export certificates for ponies were issued to American buyers. Some of these were newly inspected mares and fillies, and because some buyers could not find sufficient registered ponies a number of unregistered non-pedigree animals were shipped. The American Shetland Pony Club will not accept our pedigree ponies in their Stud Book so all shipped to the U.S.A. are taken as 'Grade' ponies.

At present there is little American demand although the odd pony now and again may be sent over, mostly probably of the very small size. It appears that there is a craze or fashion there for what is now called the 'Miniature horse', although from advertisements it appears that at least one of the stallions advertised at stud as such is an imported pedigree Shetland pony.

There has been, at times, a heavy demand from Canada, both in the early decades of this century and again at the time of the last rush of exports to the U.S.A. Canadian buyers came over here and tried to find sufficient Shetland ponies to take back: even Dartmoor was combed. Possibly this seeking out of so-called Shetland ponies from all over the country helped to improve the breed because many of the animals bought for export were cross-bred mongrels and it was to our advantage that they should be out of the country rather than allowed to breed more of the same sort. It is understood that the pony fostered by the Canadian Pony Society (founded in 1894) is very similar to the American type.

Many Shetland ponies have been exported to numerous other different and distant countries.

The countries to which ponies were being exported are not entered in the Stud Books until 1907, so unless one can gain information from private papers or correspondence it is not possible to ascertain destinations of ponies for which export certificates were issued prior to that year. In 1907 many left the country for Canada and the U.S.A. but only one went elsewhere – this was a black colt sent to Vienna by Graham Clark. In the following year, apart from those sent across the North Atlantic, South America is noted as the destination of four stallions, five colts, one mare and two fillies; actually five of those mentioned were consigned to Buenos Aires. South Africa imported two mares and one went to Germany. During these years before the 1914–18 war ponies were exported to South Africa, Argentine, Brazil and Australia as well as to Indian Rajahs and to European countries.

After the war the demand from North America decreased but there was a small but fairly constant demand from other countries. Again Indian native princes bought some while others went to Australia, South Africa, Argentine, Brazil and Columbia as well as an interesting consignment exported by Roy from Crieff in 1926 of four fillies and a colt to Weddell Island in the Falkland Group. Other unusual destinations were Constantinople, Casablanca, Barbados and Finland.

Since 1945 a few more unusual destinations appear, such as Kenya, Singapore, Egypt and Israel, whilst more than one small consignment have gone to Jamaica and to Bahrein. More recently Bermuda, Bahama and a trained gelding to Nepal are noted in Stud Book volumes, but on the whole, apart from the large number which went to North America in post-war years, European countries have imported more ponies.

Probably most ponies went to other countries not primarily for breeding or forming a stud, but as animals of unusual interest, for ornamental purposes or for children to ride and drive.

Australia is the only country, apart from those in Europe and possibly one or two exceptions, where the true type of Shetland pony is being bred. Canada and the U.S.A. have chosen to evolve their own type of small pony which has no real semblance to the true Shetland. Other countries have only a handful of ponies with no breed society to safeguard or further the breed and no rules of guidance, for there are insufficient interested persons to form such a body.

A flourishing Shetland Pony Owners and Breeders Society of Australia encourages the interests of those who keep and breed ponies and they publish a magazine – 'Ten-Two News' – to report current events and topics. The stock is registered in the Stud Book of the Australian Pony Stud Book Society who also care for the records and well-being of other breeds of ponies.

A recent issue of *Ten-Two News* contains an interesting article on the importation of Shetland ponies into Victoria. The writer states that the earliest mention she can find is of some mares and a stallion named 'Docklin' imported by a William Lyall of Hardwood, South Cranebourne, sometime during the 1850s. The author is indebted to Mrs P. B. Ronald of Victoria for a strange and probably unique sequel to this importation: in 1891 a visitor from England to Australia was so impressed by the quality of these ponies' descendants, which he saw in that country, that he bought nine and *exported* them to London.

Undoubtedly Shetlands must have been imported during the long interval between these years and the first recorded exports of registered ponies to Australia. The earliest appears to be in 1912 when two mares were sent by Mrs Beale to Mrs Maclellan, Windsor, Victoria, to be followed the following year by the stallion Halcyon (600) from Lady Estella Hope to the same buyer, who, in addition, had shipped a mare to another buyer in Victoria.

During the 1920s a number of mares and entires were exported to Australia. These included the well-known Dibblitz of Penniwells and two or three Manar bred ponies which, no doubt, were the root stock of the greys now found there.

There is obviously a strong interest in horses and ponies in a country which, particularly during the years of its emergence, was dependent on the horse and horsemastership and where, on the huge cattle and sheep stations, a horse is of prime importance. Here the true type of Shetland was fostered: a general purpose pony with a good shoulder, which will make a real riding pony for a child and will also go lightly and easily to a gig. The draught type is definitely not wanted in this circle of horsemen and women. Some of the best and very influential blood has been imported and there is no doubt that many ponies in Australia trace back to bloodlines and studs of repute. The Shetland pony is at present remarkably popular over there and of course quite rightly so. However, their root stock is limited and it must be said that some of the ponies exported from the United Kingdom were not really good enough to give a substantial foundation. Some of the bloodlines are excellent but it is doubtful whether there are sufficient. It must be remembered, also, that the distances there are huge in comparison to England. So the question of sending a mare to be served by a particular stallion may mean a round trip of two thousand miles!

If freight charges were not so high for ponies exported from this country to Australia there is little doubt that more would be purchased; but as there is little difference between the charges for a very valuable classically bred and winning thoroughbred – and a Shetland colt or stallion there is little wonder that few are now shipped or flown.

The majority of the breeding studs are in New South Wales and

Victoria, but there are also breeders in Queensland, although sub-tropical and tropical in parts, and South Australia, also, has established studs. Western Australia probably has fewer Shetlands and breeders than the other states. The societies already mentioned have both got flourishing branches in each state and local and State shows are held which include classes for Shetland ponies.

These large shows continue for up to ten days and exhibitors are required to have their stock in for the full period. This stock includes every domestic animal and every breed in the Continent. The awards at these shows rightly carry considerable prestige for the competition is very high.

There is evidence that Shetland ponies do well in Australia. The tendency to get laminitis seems to be the major trouble. This may be due to climatic conditions and the rapid growth of vegetation which may take place when rain follows a dry period or prolonged drought. In Australia the weather can be very dry for long periods which are followed by heavy rain. An animal bred for thousands of years in a much more equable climate might well be subject to disorders caused by sudden and drastic climatic changes.

It is interesting for U.K. enthusiasts to know that this continent, thousands of miles away, wishes to breed a pony of the same conformation, temperament and character as has been kept in our country for generations.

New Zealand long ago imported the odd Shetland pony, but it is doubtful whether a purebred one could still be found in the islands. Today there is little or no interest in the breed.

At one time quite a few Shetlands were bred in South America, but recently there has been little active interest displayed partly because of political and exchange difficulties. One can find references to ponies being exported in the past, some to Brazil, some to the Argentine and Lady Estella Hope shipped some.

There has been speculation amongst breeders about the prices at which ponies have been sold to foreign countries: however, as most are sold privately the figures are not usually divulged. It is known that in the 1920s an exported stallion cost £500 and that this was repeated shortly after the last war, but by a different seller and to a different destination. Since then the general value of ponies has increased enormously and some high prices have been realised both in private and auction sales.

At present the export of ponies is handicapped and made difficult by various measures which have been introduced by the Government and by penal rises in the cost of transport by road, ship and air. These restricting measures, as far as Shetland ponies are concerned, are absurd. It is foolish for valuable ponies from a well managed stud to interrupt their journey for a twelve hour period in some strange and not always satisfactory stabling, termed lairage, instead of continuing their journey in peace and comfort. It is nonsensical that a ridiculous minimum value is insisted upon whether the animal is a valuable foal which will make a stallion or breeding mare or a ten year old mare of bare minimum value. Many of these measures are suggested to and impressed on legislators (whose knowledge of the subject is little), by biased would-be humanitarians who have little practical knowledge of the transport of animals.

## *Export to Europe*

Although fewer Shetland breeding stock have been exported to Europe than to Canada and the U.S.A. a fair number have left the United Kingdom for European countries, particularly during the last twenty-five years.

Holland has been a very good customer. Although the number of ponies imported is less than the total sent to France the probable value of the stock has been higher. The Dutch breeder has always been selective requiring not only conformation and action of a high standard but also showing interest and discrimination when choosing blood-lines. Of course all ponies imported are not subjected to the same scrutiny for many ponies have been bought by Dutch dealers to sell again in other countries as well as the Netherlands. The Dutch are great exporters of livestock and if insufficient numbers are available in their own country recourse is made to the livestock market of other nations.

The commencement of export of Shetland ponies to Holland is interesting. It began on a commercial basis in the period between the wars, when laws were passed there making it illegal to use dogs for hauling of small loads, which had been the custom for many years. When this law was enforced, Shetlands took over the use of the small vehicles and the harness (possibly adapted). This was a great success for not only could the ponies pull a heavier load but they were easier and more economical to keep and feed.

In 1937 the Nederlandsch Shetland Pony Stamboek was started and although its activities were curtailed during the war it was quickly resuscitated on the cessation of hostilities. However at that time the population of ponies had been drastically reduced by the Germans.

The Dutch breeders, however, soon succeeded in setting things to rights and increasing the numbers as there was steady demand for working animals. The Shetland pony was in constant demand for all kinds of farm and horticultural work and it would be hard to name any task on farm or market garden in which these willing animals were not employed.

The Nederlandsch Stamboek has been continually active and with government aid has done much for the breed. For some years after the war the aim was to have a solid, thick, working pony modelled some-what on the lines of the Belgian horse and colour was essential in the eye of the average Dutch farmer. Some influential breeders, however, thought differently: although they recognised that the pony was for work they preferred a more active one and it did not matter whether it was coloured or black. So some owners and breeders began to favour the lighter more active type. As the pony continued to be used, it was said that if a farmer bought a tractor and got rid of his work horse he would buy a Shetland pony, if he had not already got one. For there were many jobs on the farm for which the tractor was too heavy and expensive which could easily be done by a small pony. Today, as in most countries, the use of horses and ponies has been almost entirely mechanically superseded and few are now used for farm work in Holland. However the breed is still ridden by children and driving is very popular. Large numbers are bred (in fact there is a larger population of Shetlands in Holland than there is in the United Kingdom), but still Dutch breeders come to this country to find ponies to re-export and to select some to add to their breeding studs.

Every January there are stallion shows throughout Holland and stallion owners are obliged to bring their stallions for inspection

or judging. Here they are given a I, II or III Premium or refused if
not acceptable, and unless a Premium is gained the stallion is prohibited by law from serving mares, whether of the owner or others.
All three year olds have to be submitted to this selection and only a
small proportion are passed as suitable. A really good stallion may be
given a three year Premium which means that for three years it need
not be submitted to the 'Jury'. The judging is by a 'Jury' of two
appointed by the Stud Book and a veterinary surgeon.

Every five years the Stamboek hold a two day show at s'Hertogen-
bosch for mares and fillies and for driving, riding and general showing
of Shetland ponies trained in various ways by and for children. It is
an interesting, well-managed event and, like the annual stallion show,
has been well attended by British breeders of Shetlands and by those
from other countries. The spectators observe the quality and so on of
the mares and fillies and also how well conducted is the children's
training of the ponies. All events are comparatively simple but
demonstrate clearly the mutual trust and confidence between children
and ponies.

One of the most impressive spectacles of this show is the stallion
parade. The public view over one hundred stallions being led round
the arena and then formed up, before being led round again and away.
The stallions are all in colour groups: blacks, greys and so on. Only
entires bred in the Netherlands are present – no imported ones are
there.

The Dutch export a great deal. Since they have no channel to cross
they can easily transport their exports by road to any European
country. As many cattle are also exported it is possible, and must
reduce costs, for ponies also to be included when transporting
livestock.

During the last twenty-five years France has imported more
registered Shetland ponies than any other European country but it is
unlikely that their gross value exceeds those sent to other countries.
Certainly some very good ponies have been imported into France
and the fact that chestnut is the most wanted colour must increase
their cost: the demand for chestnuts in this country has been in part
promoted by similar requirements from across the Channel. However,
there were not really enough good ponies of this colour for export and

along with some valuable and good ponies have gone some indifferent specimens. This is a pity, but when so much emphasis is placed on colour rather than on conformation and action then the resulting purchases cannot be altogether satisfactory. It is true that other colours as well as chestnut are favoured but the availability of good ponies for export is bound to be limited and possibly some of the bays and browns which have gone to France are some of the best.

There is now a French Stud Book Society for Shetland ponies and there are a few well established breeders. France is a country where, as in most other European countries other than our own, no native pony existed although there were many breeds of horse. As in other countries there was an explosion of interest in ponies and horses and mounts for excitedly interested children had to be found. Buyers from that country came over here to purchase ponies of all sizes: for the smaller children the Shetland pony was the obvious choice. Holland, as well as Britain, has exported large numbers to France.

Classes are provided for Shetland ponies at the huge Agricultural exhibition held in Paris every March. In addition there are shows in other areas and as a rule British or Dutch judges officiate.

Of all European countries which import Shetlands it is Sweden where ponies, particularly stallions, are most rigorously inspected before being accepted for their Stud Book. Although they have not imported large numbers, almost all are carefully chosen and as well as having to pass the strict examination they are required to have four generations registered in our Stud Book. The Swedish Stud Book is for other breeds as well as the Shetlands which have their own section and a Secretary to husband their interests.

Denmark, also, has import restrictions whereby only ponies of four generations in our Stud Book may be taken into the country. It, too, has fairly rigorous inspections before stallions are accepted for breeding and there the judge or inspector is usually British. The Danes have from time to time shown an interest in the Shetland, but it is only in the last twelve or thirteen years that there has been a strong demand. No doubt this also can be put down to the general explosion of interest in riding and driving.

Only during the last four or five years have Norwegians been attracted to Shetland ponies for the use of small children, as they have their own somewhat larger Fjord pony, which is also popular in Denmark. The majority of ponies exported to Norway have been those bred in Shetland as they can be flown from Sumburgh to Bergen, thus saving costs on ship and road transport. Possibly the demand in Norway may be limited though there is interest.

Belgium have a Stud book for Shetland ponies, but there are not many there and the majority are small. Many are bred from ponies sent to that country in dealers' lots, but amongst them are specially imported choices of impeccable breeding. Here, too, is a flourishing Breed Society.

West Germany has taken a few ponies from time to time, but it is much easier for them to get ponies from Holland. It seems that various German provinces have societies and sections of Stud books. At one time much work on small farms and agricultural and horticultural holdings was done by Shetlands. In some parts it is understood that a pony of 40″ or more was preferred.

It must sometimes be wondered whether British breeders of Shetland ponies are aware that there is an export market for these ponies, because often it appears that many are indifferent to what is being sought by foreign buyers. I am not implying that breeders in this country should try and change the Shetland pony to the American type or the Falabella, but as nearly all countries which do import Shetland ponies prefer the active riding and original general purpose type, their importers will not welcome a thick necked, straight shouldered animal.

Where colour is concerned most breeders in other countries prefer various colours to black, but the majority of prospective buyers do look for other good qualities also. Unfortunately they do not always get them.

It must be remembered that the pony imported is required for a definite purpose which, nine times out of ten, is to serve as a mount for a small child or to go to light harness work. This will not necessarily be the imported pony itself but its progeny in some years ahead. If the United Kingdom is to continue to export the Shetland we must send away the type and sort that is desired. We in this country are too often inclined to imagine that other countries cannot breed stock as we can. Unfortunately not all buyers are sufficiently discriminating when making a purchase and will later either become bitterly disappointed with their selection or fail to discern the difference between the good and the bad and remain in blissful ignorance.

Probably all European countries this side of the Iron Curtain have imported Shetland ponies, in varying numbers, direct from the United Kingdom. Certainly we know that in addition to the countries already mentioned, representatives of the breed have gone to Spain, Portugal, Switzerland, Austria, Italy and Finland.

These references to Shetland ponies in other countries only concern pedigree animals, but it is highly likely that in various lands throughout the world a number of unregistered and non-pedigree ponies exist. Even the number in circuses must be quite considerable.

It is always entertaining to meet people in other countries who are interested in pony or horse breeding, particularly if the language barrier can be overcome. A Federation was started for breeders to meet each other, compare conditions and so on: this was called the International Pony Breeders Federation and it held a Congress in Cologne in 1950.

A Congress was held in Edinburgh in February 1953 and the Earl of Dalkeith consented to be President. The attendance was reasonably good and visitors included both practical breeders and research and veterinary workers. Papers were read on all native breeds and on the Fjord, Iceland, and Gotland ponies, one or two papers on scientific aspects and pony breeding and population were presented and there was also a demonstration of native ponies at work.

Although interesting, it appeared that unless it appealed to more breeders the financial problem of carrying this Federation forward was bound to be severe, yet it was decided that if sufficient funds and support were forthcoming another Congress should be held. The following year one was staged at Arnhem, largely thanks to the support of the Nederlandsch S.P. Stamboek and the Dutch Government. It was a success, but too sparsely attended to make the supporters confident about continuing these functions. It was a pity that they had to lapse because they could have been a useful place to exchange knowledge. Although British ponies are presented either physically or through literature at the large Continental shows such as Paris, Essen, Frankfurt and possibly Verona, these are purely commercial ventures and scarcely fulfil the same purpose as did the Congress.

# Conclusion

Ponies in Shetland

During recent years a worldwide interest has developed in the horse and pony. Equestrian sports and pastimes have greatly increased which has meant an increase in the numbers kept to partake in these pursuits and a large increase in breeding stock to provide them.

Every succeeding year one hears of the ever-increasing interest in the Shetland pony. This has meant a proliferation of those who have decided to become owners and probably of breeders also.

These newcomers to the breed must remember that they share the responsibility of maintaining the reputation of the breed for hardiness, courage and docility and a wonderful temperament.

# Bibliography

*A Brief Description of Orkney, Zetland, Pightland Firth and Caithness,*
J.Brand 1701

*A Description of the Islands of Shetland,* Captain John Smith 1633

*A description of the Western Islands of Scotland,* to which is added
*A Brief Description of the Isles of Orkney and Shetland,* Wm.Martin
1703

*A View of the Ancient and Present State of the Zetland Isles,* D.Edmonstone 1809

*Animal Breeding,* A.L.Hagedoorn 1945

*Excavations at Jarlshof, Shetland,* J.R.C.Hamilton 1956

*Field and Fern,* The Druid (H.H.Dixon) 1865

*Historical Description of Zetland,* T.Gifford 1733

*Livestock of the Farm,* Professor C.Bryner Jones

*Ployen, C* 1840

*Shetland Advertiser* 1862

*Shetland and Its Inhabitants,* R.Cowie

*Shetland Court Books* 1602–4 and 1615–28

*Shetland Islands Pony Stud Books* 1909–12

*Shetlandponys,* Dr.Flade (Germany)

*Shetland Pony Stud Books* 1891–1974

*Statistical Account of Shetland* 1841

*The Shetland Pony,* C. & A. Douglas 1913

*The Shetland Pony,* L.F.Bedell (U.S.A.) 1960

# Index

Aberdeen 1, 26, 63, 67
Anderson, Gilbert 18, 21
Anderson, J. & Son 63, 121
Anderton, H. F. 58, 60, 63
Arab 36, 53
Argentine 125, 126, 128
Atkinson, Mrs. 68, 69, 100
Auchlochan 67, 69
Australia 68, 69, 83, 87, 125, 126, 127, 128
Austria 134
Avening 69

Baltasound 25, 32
Bathchair 18, 102
Bath & West 107
*Bazaar* 100, 105
Belgium 133
Berry 32
Betting Levy Board 33
Bowie, Dr. J. C. 60
Bot 86
Brand, J. 8, 12

Brazil 125, 128
Bressay 5, 23, 55, 57
Bronze Age 4
Bruce Mrs. 57
Bruce, John, of Sumburgh 18, 61
Bruce, R. H. W. of Sand Lodge 32, 61
Bruises 83
Brydon, Robert 18
Bryner Jones, Prof. C. 22, 47, 103

Canada 1, 20, 121, 125, 126
Celtic 4, 5
Clark, Graham 67, 125
Christopherson, Miss S. 69
Clibberswick 32
Coal mines 15, 16
Colours 39, 45, 53, 90
Columbia 126
Colvadale 30
Congested Districts 21

Cossar Ewart, J. 4
Court Books 6, 7
Cox, Mrs M. 69, 100
Crofters Commission 32, 33, 34

Dean, J. 28, 33
Denmark 119, 132, 133
Department of Agriculture
   for Scotland 10, 23, 24, 26,
   27, 28, 29, 33, 36, 51, 52
Dick, Mrs. W. 66
Dick, D. W. H. 66
Douglas, Charles 22, 37, 47,
   48, 49, 67, 111
Driving 98, 99, 100
Druid, The (H. H. Dixon) 15,
   16, 22, 39
Ducker, Mrs. 69, 100
Duffus, Mrs. Etta 67, 68

Earlshall 64, 65, 66, 68, 69
Edmonston, Dr. L. 10, 13, 16,
   22, 36, 58
Epsom Salts 87
Eshaness 29

Fair Isle 61
Falkland Islands 126
Feeding 74, 75, 76, 79, 114
Feet 40, 53, 81, 82
Felbridge 69
Fetlar 23, 25, 26, 29, 30, 33, 36
Finland 134
Foals 16, 39, 41, 44, 49, 74, 77,
   78, 79
Foaling 72, 77, 78
Foal Sales 35

France 131, 132

Germany, West 125
Gifford, Thomas 8
Glasier, Miss E. 69
Gore-Langton, Lady Joan 61
Gourlay, F. N. M. 58, 66, 67, 68

Hagedoorn, Prof. 51
Haldor(270) 60, 63
Harviestoun 66, 68, 69
Heoghs 32
Hibbert, Samuel, M.D. 9, 94
Hobart, Lady 66, 100
Holland 103, 119, 120, 129,
   130, 133
Hope, Lady Estella 47, 56, 57,
   58, 59, 61, 69, 99, 127, 128
Hope-Johnstone, Mrs. Went-
   worth 57, 99
Houldsworth, Col. Sir. R. 68
Houldsworth, Mrs. 68

Ickworth 13
International Horse Show 100
International Pony Breeders
   Federation 134
Italy 134

Jack(16) 56, 57, 60
Judges 109, 110, 111, 115, 117

Kerr, J. E. 68
Klibber 92, 94

Laird of Noss(20) 56, 66
Laminitis 86

Lerwick 3, 13, 14, 25
Lice 83
Livestock Inspector 28, 33, 51
Londonderry, Marquis of 17,
    18, 22, 55, 61
Londonderry Stud 23, 50, 57,
    59, 62
Long reining 97
Lord of the Isles(26) 56, 62
Lunging 96

MacKenzie, R. W .R. 21, 22,
    47, 58, 59, 60, 64, 65
Magazine 19, 105, 119
Mainland 19, 25, 29, 32, 39, 55
Manson, Anderson 18, 21, 58,
    62, 121
Manson, Peter 62, 63, 66
Marshwood 66, 69, 105
Maryfield 62, 63, 69
Meiklejohn, J. J. R. 18
'Miniature' 47, 48
Ministry of Agriculture 52
Mousa 61
Muness 30
Mungall, Wm. 58, 62, 66
Myles, T. H. F. 19, 29

National Pony Society 48, 108
Nederlandsch Shetland Pony
    Stamboek 130
Nesting 7, 29, 32
Netherley 69
Nicholson, Sir A. 36
Nicholson, Sir S. 33
Norway 6, 132

Odin(32) 50, 56, 59, 60, 62, 66
Oman(33) 59, 60
Ordale 32
Orkney 6, 13, 15

Papil Stone 5
Patterson, D. M. 19
Peat flitting 92, 94
Penniwells 67, 68, 69
Pit ponies 15, 17, 46, 58, 103
Ployen, C. 14
Pneumonia 87
Premium Stallion Scheme 26,
    28, 29, 34
Prince of Thule(36) 50, 56, 59

Queen Victoria 15, 56, 59

Ritchie, Miss A. R. 69
Royal Agricultural Society
    of England 108
Royal Highland & Agricultural
    Society of Scotland 108

Sandison, Alex. 18, 61, 62, 64
Sandison, Ian E. M. 14, 22, 61
Scattalds 27, 29, 30, 32, 34, 38,
    41
Seaham Harbour 17, 57, 66
Seaweed 37, 40, 41
Service 80, 81
Shearer, Mrs. 69
Shetland Pony Breeders Club
    19
Shetland Pony Stud Book
    Society 18, 27, 28, 29, 35, 43,
    51, 60, 68, 80, 101, 105, 120

S.P.S-B. Society's Council 19, 20, 28, 47, 61
Shetland Pony Stud Book 18, 19, 21, 33, 49, 55, 56, 58, 63, 68, 70
Shetland Islands 2, 24, 28, 34, 37, 39, 70
Shetland Islands Pony Stud Book Society 20, 21, 121
Show tack 115, 116
Smith, Capt. J. 8
Smith, John 22, 32, 37
South America 125, 128
Spain 134
Statistical Account 9
Standen 69
Strains 83
Strapping 112
Sweden 119, 132
Sweet Itch 82
Switzerland 134

Thoreau(392) 60
Thor(83) 62

Training 91, 95, 98, 114
Transy 60, 66, 69
Travel tetany 87

United States of America 15, 20, 39, 55, 61, 120, 124, 126
Unst 1, 7, 9, 16, 19, 23, 25, 29, 30, 33, 47, 61
Uyeasound 30, 61, 64

Vaila 63
Vikings 5, 120

Wainwright 5
Walker, R. W. 19
Walls 23, 63
Washing 112
Water 72, 75
Weaning 78, 79
Westing 23, 30
Woodbury 69
Worms 84, 85, 86

Yell 30